A CUPBEARER CALLED NEHEMIAH

THE CALLED
BOOK 10

KENNETH A. WINTER

WildernessLessons

JOIN MY READERS' GROUP FOR UPDATES AND FUTURE RELEASES

Please join my Readers' Group so i can send you a free book, as well as updates and information about future releases, etc.

See the back of the book for details on how to sign up.

A Cupbearer Called Nehemiah

The Called – Book 10 (a series of novellas)

Published by:

Kenneth A. Winter

WildernessLessons, LLC

Richmond, Virginia

United States of America

kenwinter.org

wildernesslessons.com

Edited by Sheryl Martin Hash

Cover design by Scott Campbell Design

ISBN 978-1-9568662-0-9 (soft cover)

ISBN 978-1-9568662-1-6 (e-book)

ISBN 978-1-9568662-2-3 (large print)

Library of Congress Control Number: 2023907990

The basis for the story line of this book is taken from the Books of *Nehemiah, Ezra and Esther in* the Holy Bible. Certain fictional events or depictions of those events have been added.

Unless otherwise indicated, all Scripture quotations are taken from the *Holy Bible*, New Living Translation, copyright © 1996. Used by permission of Tyndale House Publishers, Inc., Wheaton, Illinois 60189. All rights reserved.

Scripture quotations marked (CEV) are from the Contemporary English Version Copyright © 1991, 1992, 1995 by American Bible Society, Used by Permission.

Scripture quotations marked (ESV) are taken from *The Holy Bible, English Standard Version*, copyright © 2001 by Crossway, a publishing ministry of Good News Publishers. Used by permission. All rights reserved.

Scripture quotations marked (NIV) are taken from *The Holy Bible, New International Version*® NIV® Copyright © 1973, 1978, 1984, 2011 by Biblica, Inc. ™ Used by permission. All rights reserved worldwide.

DEDICATION

To
Weston Zion,
a precious gift from the Lord

❧

Trust in the Lord with all your heart;
do not depend on your own understanding.
Seek His will in all you do,
and He will show you which path to take.
(Proverbs 3:5-6)

❧

CONTENTS

PREFACE

~

This fictional novella is the tenth book in the series titled, *The Called*. Like the others, it is a story about an ordinary person who surrendered his life to God and was called by Him to be used in extraordinary ways. As i've said in my previous books, we tend to elevate the people we read about in Scripture and place them on a pedestal far beyond our reach because of the faith they exhibited. But Nehemiah would tell us that, left to his own devices, he could never have accomplished on his own what God did through him.

In that respect, his story is very similar to most of ours. He found himself in a situation and a position in which God chose to use him. He was there because God had ordered his steps to be there. He would tell you that the boldness with which he first approached his king came directly from God. He would not have had the courage to make that first request apart from God's prompting, strength, and favor. He was a servant whom God had permitted to rise through the ranks – in a way similar to that of Joseph, the son of Jacob, who ultimately rose from being a slave and a prisoner to becoming a prime minister of Egypt.

The story line is, of course, taken from the books of Nehemiah and Ezra in the Holy Bible. There are elements from the Book of Esther that also inform the story. As you probably know, Nehemiah was the cupbearer to the king. He had earned the trust of the king. Literally, King Artaxerxes entrusted his life to Nehemiah each and every day. Nehemiah was expected to always be by the king's side. As a result, the two men developed a unique bond as servant and king. The trust between them would have more than likely evolved into a friendship of sorts, despite their respective stations.

Bear in mind that the portion of Nehemiah's story leading up to that fateful day – when he learns from his brother about the conditions in Jerusalem – has been created from my imagination. We have no idea what circumstances led to his becoming the king's cupbearer. We do know that he was permitted to be in the queen's presence, which would imply that he was uniquely fitted for that role. This is my effort to take what we know and craft a plausible story that provides insight into what his life may have been like prior to what is recorded in the Book of Nehemiah.

We also know that Nehemiah was in Jerusalem for twelve years after the wall was rebuilt, then was recalled to Susa by the king. He was gone from Jerusalem for several years, though the exact amount of time is unknown. Those years of his absence occur between chapters 12 and 13 of the Book of Nehemiah.

We do not know what he did during that time. However, it is highly unlikely he returned to the role of cupbearer. His accomplishments in Jerusalem would have led to his being given a different position in the king's court. Though many events depicted in this story are fictional, the work of restoration in other cities within the Persian Empire during Artaxerxes' reign is well documented.

So, i invite you to sit back and join Nehemiah as he shares his unique story, along with other characters who were an important part of his journey. You will recognize many of their names from Scripture. As in all my books, i have added background details about some of them that are not in Scripture, so we might see them as people and not just names.

i have also added fictional characters to round out the story, and i have given names to those we know existed but remained unnamed in the Bible. They represent the many people who would have surrounded Nehemiah during his lifetime. Included as an appendix in the back of this book is a character listing to clarify the historical vs. fictional elements of each character.

Whenever i directly quote Scripture, it is italicized. The Scripture references are also included as an appendix in the book. The remaining instances of dialogue not italicized are a part of the fictional story that helps advance the narrative.

My hope is this book will prompt you to turn to the Books of Nehemiah, Ezra, and Esther and reread the biblical account of Nehemiah's life and the events surrounding it. As you do, you will be reminded of the way God worked through this ordinary man to accomplish an extraordinary task. None of my books is intended to be a substitute for God's Word – rather, i hope they will lead you to spend time in His Word.

Finally, my prayer is you will see Nehemiah through fresh eyes – and be challenged to live out *your* walk with the Lord with the same conviction, courage, and faith he displayed. And most importantly, i pray you will be challenged to be an "ordinary" follower with the willingness and faith to be used by God in extraordinary ways – that will impact not only this generation, but also the generations to come . . . until our Lord returns!

❧

1

A VISITOR AT THE GATE

～

I remember that day as if it were yesterday. It rained that morning for the first time in months. The rain freshened the air and brought relief from the long summer's heat and dryness. The change in the air had quickened my step, and as I moved about the palace in Susa, I was certain that was true for most everyone else as well.

I fully expected it to be a quiet day in the palace. There were no festivities or royal functions planned. The king had just returned from a weeklong hunt and intended to rest for several days. The fact that he had just returned meant that I also had just returned. You see, as the king's cupbearer, I was always by his side. I served him in that capacity for nigh on eighteen years.

I would have willingly sacrificed my life for my king. There was no food or drink that passed through his lips that I did not first inspect and make sure was safe for him to consume. I selected his wines and foods based upon what I knew to be his preferences. And I kept careful watch over his meal preparation, and occasionally sampled his food or beverages to ensure they were acceptable. Over the years, we assembled a trusted cadre of cooks, bakers, kitchen workers, gamekeepers, and farmers. They were well aware of the penalty should they ever endanger the king's health or life.

Because the king entrusted me with his life, a unique bond of trust developed between us over the years. It didn't start out that way, but as time passed, the king felt free to say things to me that he would never have uttered in front of his most trusted advisors. He knew that I knew my place. He never asked me for advice; rather, I was simply a trusted confidant with whom he could express his most personal thoughts without fear of them being repeated. Eventually, the king told me his most confidential plans for the kingdom and his people – long before he shared them with anyone in his court.

My life revolved around my service to him. I was always nearby and available at a moment's notice. I never ventured from the palace unless I was in the company of the king, and I had no friendships or close relationships apart from my allegiance to him.

That's why I was so surprised when I received word I had a visitor waiting at the palace gates. I had lived in the palace for thirty-four years and never once had anyone come to see me. I could not imagine who it might be, and the servant who delivered the message was unable to shed any light on who it might be. Since the visitor was unannounced, the royal guards had prevented him from entering the gates.

As I approached the guards, they came to attention. Even though I held no position of rank over them, the guards – as well as all the servants – treated me with a respect beyond my station because of my unique relationship with the king. In fact, I frequently noticed they treated me with more respect than they showed some of the king's less gentlemanly royal counselors.

The guard pointed out a man standing outside the gate with his back to me. I could see he was about my same build. His cloak was well-worn and bore the signs of one who had just traveled a long distance. As I passed through the gate, he turned toward me. His hair and beard had obviously once been like coal, but now they were being overtaken by gray. He looked like a man who regularly engaged in physical labor. I did not recognize him, which made me even more curious as to why he had come to see me.

But as our eyes met, I began to sense something familiar about him. His eyes were the same as mine, not only in color but also in expression. The man approached me and threw his arms around me in an embrace.

"Brother," he exclaimed, "it has been a long time! I doubt I would have known you if I wasn't waiting for you here at the gate. You are quite the distinguished gentleman. And I fear you do not recognize me."

"You are correct, friend," I said, as I pulled away from his embrace. "Who are you and why have you asked to see me?"

"Nehemiah," he replied, "I am your brother, Hanani!"

Hanani? Though the name was familiar, I had not heard his name or thought of him – or any of my brothers – for many years. I did not know if any of them, or my father, were even still alive.

They had all abandoned me when I was eight years old. They had returned to our ancestral city and left me here. In thirty-four years, I had never received one word from them. I was left to be raised by people who were not my family, but who had become my family.

And by the grace and mercy of Jehovah God, those who had raised me did not teach me to worship the false gods of the Persians. Rather, I had been instructed in the law of Moses and the ways of my ancestors. I had been taught to love and obey Jehovah God, and He – unlike my family – had never abandoned me.

But now, as I looked into my oldest brother's eyes, I saw a tear roll down his cheek. "Nehemiah," he said, "our father has died. Though I know you probably believe he never loved you, that is not true. He left you here – we all left you here – because he wanted to protect you. He was an honorable man who loved and obeyed our God. That is why he went to Jerusalem and took us with him, but left you here.

"Allow me to honor our father by telling you your story . . . perhaps parts of which you don't remember or have never known."

～

A PASSION IS KINDLED

❦

*H*anani began, "When Nebuchadnezzar, king of the Chaldeans, conquered Jerusalem, he destroyed our magnificent Temple erected by King Solomon. He also demolished many other buildings and tore down large segments of the wall surrounding the city to ensure it could not be easily rebuilt.

"With much of the city now in ruins, he deported the most prominent citizens of Judah – the wealthy, the religious leaders, the influential, and the craftsmen – to Babylon. He rightly assumed that without anyone left to lead them, those who remained in Jerusalem would make no attempt to rebuild the city. Judah ceased to exist as an independent kingdom. The people who remained there lived in the squalor of destruction and devastation, an ever-present reminder of their defeat.

"Many of the people began to question their relationship with Jehovah God and their position as 'God's chosen people.' But others knew their relationship with Him did not end with the destruction of the Temple and the burning of Jerusalem. They believed the exile was the dawn of a new beginning. They held onto God's promise through the prophet Jeremiah: *'For I know the plans I have for you. They are plans for good and not for disaster, to give you a future and a hope.'*[1]

"What most of the people saw as devastation, that remnant saw as an opportunity. With most of the landholders deported to Babylon, the people who remained had the opportunity to lay claim to those abandoned holdings and begin a new life. Our grandfather Ezer's parents were among them."

Hanani went on to explain that prior to the exile, my great-grandparents had worked in servitude as spinners and weavers of fabric – in order to pay off their indebtedness to one of the most successful merchants in the city. With him now in exile, my great-grandparents were no longer under the burden of that debt. Though his buildings had been destroyed, the merchant's spindles and looms had somehow miraculously survived.

Even defeated people need clothing, so our great-grandparents laid claim to those tools and built a makeshift workplace on land that had been occupied by the merchant. The Chaldeans let them be as long as they did not attempt to rebuild any buildings or repair the wall.

Though most residents of the city didn't have significant financial means, our great-grandparents made more money working in these conditions than they ever had as servants. Within a short time, they were making a modest living. They lived in a makeshift home on the same property as their business.

Many of those who remained in Jerusalem lost their faith in Jehovah God, believing He no longer had the power to protect them. They either forgot – or chose to forget – that it was their disobedience to God that had led to their defeat and captivity. Instead, they turned to the pagan gods of the Chaldeans and Babylonians. Thankfully, our great-grandparents were not among them. They continued to faithfully follow Jehovah God and obey His laws.

Since all the priests were gone and the Temple was destroyed, most of the written Scripture was no longer accessible in the city. So the people repeated the teachings they had memorized as children – in particular, those found in the writings of the prophet Isaiah. This one gave them the greatest hope:

> *"Sing, O heavens, for the Lord has done this wondrous thing.*
> *Shout for joy, O depths of the earth!*
> *Break into song, O mountains and forests and every tree!*
> *For the Lord has redeemed Jacob and is glorified in Israel.*
>
> *"This is what the Lord says — your Redeemer and Creator:*
> *'I am the Lord, who made all things. I alone stretched out the heavens.*
> *Who was with Me when I made the earth?*
> *I expose the false prophets as liars and make fools of fortune-tellers.*
> *I cause the wise to give bad advice, thus proving them to be fools.*
>
> *"'But I carry out the predictions of My prophets!*
> *By them I say to Jerusalem, "People will live here again,"*
> *and to the towns of Judah, "You will be rebuilt;*
> *I will restore all your ruins!"'"*[2]

Our great-grandparents' hope was stirred even more by two events. The first was the news that the Chaldeans had been conquered by the Persians. There were indications that the Persian king, Cyrus the Great, may be more sympathetic to the plight of the Judahites.

Those signs proved to be true when, less than a year later, Cyrus commissioned a contingent of carpenters and laborers to return to Jerusalem from Babylon to rebuild the Temple. He sent Zerubbabel – the grandson of the last king of Judah – to lead the effort and designated him the new governor of the province of Judah.

The second event was the birth of their son Ezer. They were confident the kingdom of Judah would reemerge in his generation, and they reared him in the promises and ways of Jehovah God. From the moment Ezer could speak, our great-grandparents taught him all the Scriptures they could remember. On the Sabbath, they transformed their workplace into a place of worship, and several other like-minded families joined them. Though restoration of the Temple was now underway, they continued to be cautious around their Persian overseers and never referred to their gathering place as a synagogue.

Two of the men who, together with their families, joined them each Sabbath were Jair and his younger brother, Abihail, from the tribe of Benjamin. Both men were the grandsons of a successful merchant named Kish, who was taken into exile by Nebuchadnezzar. However, Kish had been able to keep the identity of his son, Shimei, secret from the Chaldeans. Shimei escaped exile and remained in Jerusalem. He, and eventually his sons, Jair and Abihail, carried on Kish's trade on a reduced scale so as not to draw the Chaldeans' attention during those early years.

Jair had a son named Mordecai who was slightly younger than Ezer and Abihail. The three boys soon became fast friends and challenged one another in their knowledge of the Scriptures. The more they studied the prophecies of Isaiah, the more they became convinced that Jehovah God had orchestrated for their families to remain in Jerusalem to help restore the city and the kingdom. And they believed that under the rule of the Persians, the time had come. Despite their fathers' concerns of possible Persian retaliation, the three young men exuberantly voiced their belief to others.

Even after Ezer and Abihail both married, their daring and passion continued to escalate. The births of Ezer's son Hacaliah and Abihail's daughter Hadassah seemed to bolster their resolve even further. Both of them, together with Mordecai, began to zealously advocate for the restoration of the kingdom of Judah. They were confident Jehovah God would grant them success.

However, their actions rose to the level that even Zerubbabel could no longer overlook them as youthful zeal. Restoring the Temple was one thing; openly advocating the restoration of the kingdom of Judah was quite another. That would be seen by the Persians as treason! Though Zerubbabel prayed silently for that outcome, he feared the young men's rebellious actions would set back the progress being made.

Zerubbabel had the men and their families taken into custody and transported as captives to Susa. During their journey, the three friends cried out to God asking why He had given them a passion to restore the kingdom, only to allow them to be thwarted. The heavens were silent, and they continued to await their answer as they made their way to Susa.

∽

3

THE EARLY DAYS IN SUSA

∽

$\mathcal{B}$y the time the captives' caravan arrived in Susa, King Darius had succeeded King Cyrus's eldest son, Cambyses, on the Persian throne. Darius had quickly demonstrated his intention to govern with a more conciliatory touch than his predecessors. Instead of the confinement Ezer, Abihail, and Mordecai feared, the magistrate who ruled on the charges against them released them to live and work in the city with one stipulation – they could not leave Susa.

All three men set about making a living in order to provide for their families. Ezer and his son Hacaliah reestablished themselves as respected weavers of the finest fabrics. Mordecai, who never married, was a shrewd trader of goods and soon found a lucrative opportunity trading at the city gate. He also became well-known by the city elders, who sat at the gate to dispense their wisdom.

Abihail followed in his father's footsteps by establishing himself as a merchant of spices. Sadly, he and his wife contracted a severe lung infection shortly after their arrival and died. Their daughter Hadassah, who was not affected by the disease, was taken in by her cousin Mordecai as his adopted daughter.

As time passed, Hacaliah married a young woman named Hadiya from the tribe of Judah. She had grown up as an exile in Susa. The couple had five sons – Hanani was the oldest and I was the youngest. Sadly, I never knew my mother since she died giving birth to me. Hanani told me I inherited my empathy and determination from her.

As Hanani continued to recount my story, some of those distant memories returned to me. By the time I was old enough to walk and talk, my father and grandfather had told me countless stories about the history of our people. I knew Jehovah God had freed our people from the bondage of Egypt and led them to the land He had promised them. I knew He led our people to become one of the wealthiest and most admired nations under the reign of King Solomon. But I also knew that King Solomon had turned away from God in his later years, setting in motion the events that would eventually lead to our exile.

I also remembered my grandfather telling me many stories about the beauty and wonders of Jerusalem and the majesty of the Temple that had been erected during King Solomon's reign. I grieved with my grandfather every time he spoke of the city's – and even more specifically, the Temple's – destruction.

I would join my grandfather in praying for the reestablishment of the Temple and our city. One day, my grandfather joyfully announced, "King Darius has issued orders acknowledging the decree proclaimed by King Cyrus. The decree says, '*The Temple of God at Jerusalem must be rebuilt on the site where Jews used to offer their sacrifices. The full construction costs are to be paid without delay from my taxes collected in the province so that the work can be completed.*'[1]

"The work on the Temple has languished far too long," my grandfather said, "lacking the financial resources and labor to complete the construction. The workers long ago became discouraged. But now the king has authorized the work and committed to pay for it out of his own treasury! Praise be to Jehovah God, Nehemiah, for He has answered our prayers!"

Soon thereafter, King Darius's health declined, leading to his death. His son, Xerxes, whom some called Ahasuerus, ascended to his father's throne. Thankfully, he continued his father's support of the work in Jerusalem. His wife, Vashti, became queen. Hanani reminded me that she was the great-granddaughter of the Babylonian king, Nebuchadnezzar. Everyone thought it ironic that her great-grandfather was the king who destroyed the Temple – and now her husband as king was rebuilding it.

"When you were five years old," Hanani told me, "soon after our grandfather died, something happened at the palace that you were too young to understand. I'm not certain those of us who were older truly understood the impact that event would have on all our futures.

"King Xerxes was holding a banquet for all the male palace servants and officials, while Queen Vashti was holding a separate banquet for the women of the palace. It was on the heels of a great celebration that had lasted for six months. On the seventh day of the banquet, when the king had been drinking excessively, he summoned his queen to present herself before him in the great hall and display her beauty to his guests. The queen refused, provoking Xerxes's anger.

"When the king asked his advisers how Vashti should be punished for her disobedience, they replied, '*Queen Vashti has wronged not only the king but also every official and citizen throughout your empire. Women everywhere will begin to despise their husbands when they learn that the queen has refused to appear before her king. So if it pleases the king, we suggest you issue a written decree that Queen Vashti be forever banished from your presence and that you choose another queen more worthy than she.*'[2]

"The king agreed with his advisers, and Vashti was immediately banished. A few days later, once his anger had diminished, the king began to mourn the companionship of his beautiful queen. Seeing his distress, his attendants suggested, *'Let us search the empire to find beautiful young virgins for the king to choose from. The young woman who pleases you most will be made queen instead of Vashti.'*[3]

"One of the young women selected by the king's attendants was Hadassah, the adopted daughter of Mordecai. He advised her to conceal her nationality and family background, and use only her Persian name – Esther. When she and the other young women were brought to the king's fortress, they were placed under the charge of Hegai, the eunuch, who oversaw the king's royal harem.

"Hegai was immediately drawn to Esther and treated her with great kindness. He took special care in helping her prepare to go before the king, and she heeded his counsel in every detail. On the night Esther was taken to the king's bed chamber, the king loved her more than the other young women brought before him. He was so delighted with Esther, in fact, that he set the royal crown on her head without delay and declared her to be his queen.

"To celebrate the occasion, he gave a banquet for all his princes and servants, and declared a public festival to be observed throughout the provinces in her honor."

4

A SERVANT TO THE QUEEN

~

*A*s Hanani continued telling my story, memories vividly returned to me. I recalled the night my father informed my brothers and me, "A group of men is planning to leave for Jerusalem in a few days to help rebuild the city. I have spoken to the city officials, and since your grandfather has died, we are no longer required to remain here in the city. We are free to travel back to Jerusalem and assist in the effort. So Hanani, I want you to make sure your brothers are ready to make the trip . . . except for Nehemiah."

"Why am I not going, father?" I asked.

"Because we are going to do men's work," my father replied, "and you are not yet big enough or strong enough."

"Father, I am already eight years old," I countered, straining to make myself look taller and bigger.

"I know you are, Nehemiah," he said gently, "and because of that, I have something special I need you to do. I have spoken to Mordecai, and he agrees it would be a good idea for you to become a servant to Queen Hadassah. That way, you can help him keep a close eye on her and make sure she remains safe. No one yet knows that she is a Jew, and he wants it to stay that way."

"But, father, how long will you and my brothers be gone?"

"I do not know, my son, but one day I will return for you," he answered. "In the meantime, I need you to carry out this important task to help watch over the queen."

"I will, father," I replied, trying to hold back tears. "I will watch her closely and protect her until you return."

Though I was young – and felt abandoned – I knew deep down my father was leaving me in Susa for my safety. My brothers were old enough to take care of themselves – and life in Jerusalem would be hard. My father had decided that the palace would be the safest place for me during his absence. And he knew Mordecai and the queen would watch out for me.

The next day, my father took me to the palace to see Hegai, just as Mordecai had arranged. Hegai was no longer the overseer of the royal harem; he was now serving Queen Esther as her chief steward. I would be under his charge. All the queen's servants were women except for two young men besides me. I was by far the youngest of them all.

I asked if I would see the queen that day, but I was told there was one detail that needed to be taken care of before I could serve in her court. If my father knew what that detail was, he hadn't told me.

Soon after my father left, Hegai told me all male servants to the queen – aged eight and above – must be eunuchs. It was true of the others, including him, and now it must be true of me. I wasn't given any time to fully understand what was about to happen to me or what the long-term effects would be. Rather, I had been brought to the palace to be a servant to the queen – and that required me to become a eunuch.

It was probably a good thing I wasn't given time to consider what was about to occur. Gratefully, the one who performed the deed did so with the greatest of care. Hegai and the other servants were kind as they cared for me in the days that followed.

Once I was healed enough to be put to work, I was summoned by the queen. I had not seen her since she was taken from the Jewish quarter and brought to the palace. As I entered the grand chamber of her royal suite, I bowed in the manner Hegai had instructed me. I kept my eyes averted as I made my way toward her. I stopped in the center of the room until she summoned me to draw closer.

But my initial glimpse revealed her sitting on an ornate chair at the far end of the room. I had been told this was the room she used to meet with her visitors. I had never seen such a grand room! Hegai had explained that the doorway leading from that room opened into her private sitting chamber and from there into her bed chamber. He cautioned that I would never be permitted to go into her bed chamber, and would most often attend her in this formal meeting room.

Once I was just a few feet from the queen, I stopped, bowed again, and waited for her to speak. Hegai had warned me to never speak first, but only when I was spoken to – and then only to answer a question asked of me. "Welcome, Nehemiah," the queen said. "You may look up at me. I want to see your face."

Truth be told, if I hadn't known who she was, I never would have recognized her. She looked so regal – nothing like the carefree, fun-loving girl I remembered. I was immediately struck by her beauty, though I had never noticed when we lived next door to one another. I was suddenly in awe of her.

She must have sensed my discomfort, because she smiled at me and whispered, "Do not be frightened of me, Nehemiah. I am your queen, and you are now one of my servants. But never forget that first we were friends, and I am grateful to have a friend now serving me. We must always follow the protocol that Hegai is teaching you, and we can never openly talk about our days living in the quarter. But know that I have not forgotten. As my servant, you will serve and watch out for me. And know that as your queen and friend, I will watch out for you.

"I regret the price you had to pay to serve me here in the palace. We have all made sacrifices we never intended. But we are all walking in the ways that Jehovah God set before us. We may never know why, but we must always trust Him. As my cousin Mordecai often tells me, '*Who can say but that you have been elevated to the palace for just such a time as this?*"[1]

5

A SINISTER PLOT

~

*M*ordecai came to see the queen soon after my arrival. I was attending to the queen in her private sitting chamber when he announced he had an urgent message. "Two of the king's private guards are plotting to assassinate him," he declared. "You must warn the king of their plan!"

Queen Esther reported the threat to the king, being careful to credit Mordecai for the information. King Xerxes ordered an investigation immediately and quickly discovered the report was true. The two men were hanged on the gallows without delay. The king commanded that Mordecai's act of allegiance be recorded in the royal book of decrees and commendations, but nothing further was done to reward him.

Sometime later, King Xerxes named Haman, an Amalekite, as prime minister. In this role, only the king had a higher rank than him. Haman was unable to hide his delight when the king further commanded that all of his officials would bow before their prime minister to show respect.

Haman was a descendant of Agag, the king of the Amalekites. Agag had initiated an unprovoked attack against our people many years earlier as they journeyed through the wilderness. God had given our people victory that day as Moses held up his staff on a hill overlooking the battle. And God had continued to give us victory over them through King David. The Amalekites held great resentment for our people, and they had openly declared the Jews to be their sworn enemy.

That hatred was deeply instilled in Haman, and he believed it was his destiny to retaliate and destroy our people once and for all. He made no secret of his Amalekite heritage, conspicuously wearing his tribal amulet over his robes. Neither did he make any secret of his disdain for the Jewish people.

As a result, Mordecai refused to obey the king's command to bow before this enemy of the Jews. Those who sat with him at the city gate reported his conduct to Haman, who became enraged. He was so angry that, instead of punishing Mordecai only, he decided to destroy all the Jews living throughout the empire.

After craftily convincing the king that the Jews were a threat against his rule, Haman issued a decree throughout the empire, that all Jews were to be slaughtered on a single day – the fourteenth day of Adar – of the year following the mandate. The decree was carried by messengers into all the provinces of the empire.

When Mordecai learned about the mandate, he tore his clothes, put on sackcloth and ashes, and stood outside the palace gates wailing bitterly. Two of the queen's maids informed her of Mordecai's actions, and she became greatly perplexed, not having knowledge of the decree. She instructed me to go to Mordecai and find out what was troubling him.

As I approached him, I became frightened by the depth of his pain and sorrow. I momentarily stopped and stood at a distance. When Mordecai saw me, he ceased his cries, and motioned for me to approach.

"Has the queen sent you?" he asked.

"Yes, she has," I replied. "She wants to know what is troubling you and why you are in mourning."

Mordecai handed me a copy of Haman's decree and told me to take it to the queen. "Tell her I said, 'She must go to the king and beg for mercy for her people,'" he implored.

When I conveyed Mordecai's message to the queen, she looked as if I had struck a dagger through her heart. I could see the despair on her face. She sat quietly as she considered the implications of what she had heard.

Finally, she spoke to me. "Return to Mordecai and relay this message: '*The whole world knows that anyone who appears before the king in his inner court without being invited is doomed to die unless the king holds out his gold scepter. And the king has not called me to come to him in more than a month.*'"[1]

When I returned to Mordecai, he told me, "I have received a message from your father today. He says, 'When the messengers arrived in Jerusalem, the entire city fell into confusion. Since the decree states our people are not permitted to defend ourselves, the entire city has become paralyzed in fear. Their fear has led to mourning, which has now led to complete resignation.

"'A belief has settled over our people,' he continued, 'that nothing can be done, and Jehovah God has abandoned us. The people have begun to do what is right in their own eyes. They neglect anything having to do with God, and corruption has taken over the city.'

"You must take this reply back to the queen," Mordecai instructed. "Tell her I have said, '*Do not think for a moment that you will escape there in the palace when all other Jews are killed. If you keep quiet at a time like this, deliverance for the Jews will arise from some other place, but you and your relatives will die. What's more, who can say but that you have been elevated to the palace for just such a time as this?'*"[2]

As I relayed the message to Queen Esther, I saw fear in her eyes for the first and only time I would ever see it from her. But that was quickly replaced with a look of determination. "Go tell Mordecai, '*Gather together all the Jews of Susa and fast for me. Do not eat or drink for three days, night or day. My servants and I will do the same. And then, though it is against the law, I will go in to see the king. If I must die, I am willing to die.'*"[3]

We all began to fast.

6

AN UNLIKELY BOND

~

*A*fter three days had passed, the queen put on her royal robes and made her way to the inner court of the palace, located just across from the king's hall. Hegai attempted to dissuade her from taking the risk. But she knew it was what Jehovah God would have her do. She instructed the rest of us to continue with the preparations she had given us.

The king was seated on his royal throne facing the entrance. When he saw Queen Esther, he welcomed her, holding out his gold scepter to her. The queen slowly approached and touched its tip.

"What do you want, my queen?" the king asked. *"What is your request? I will give it to you, even if it is half the kingdom!"*[1]

"If it please the king, let the king and Haman come today to a banquet I have prepared for the king,"[2] she replied.

The story is well documented in other accounts of how God opened the king's eyes to Haman's deception through the queen's brave actions, prompting the king to order Haman's public execution.[3] At the same time, the Spirit of God reminded the king of Mordecai's heroic actions to thwart the earlier assassination attempt. So King Xerxes honored Mordecai by elevating him to the newly vacated position of prime minister.

Mordecai's first request as the new prime minister was for the king to issue a decree giving the Jews authority to unite to defend themselves against attack. Sensing the king's earnestness to protect the Jewish people, all of his commanders, as a show of support for their king, took up arms to defend the Jews. They pledged to annihilate any enemy that attempted to harm them.

The crisis was averted, and our people celebrated throughout Jerusalem and the entire Persian Empire. As a result, a revival took place among our people and there was a renewed devotion to God and His Law among the Jews. Sadly, however, those of us in Susa soon learned this newfound devotion was short-lived in the city of Jerusalem. Generations of pagan worship and disregard for God's Law continued to cloud the judgment of those who lived there.

Because of Queen Esther and Mordecai's influence on King Xerxes, our people began to enjoy greater religious freedoms than we had since captivity. This prompted a renewed interest among our religious leaders in Susa to safeguard the teachings of Moses and the prophets.

Mordecai helped establish an assembly of Jewish leaders, rabbis, and prophets in Susa called the Great Synagogue. Their purpose was to safeguard the Torah and other sacred writings of the prophets, canonizing them into Scripture, and teaching the people about our God and His covenant with us.

~

Prince Artaxerxes was the son of King Xerxes and his first queen, Vashti. The prince was a young boy when his mother was banished from the realm. Though Xerxes loved his son, he placed his responsibilities as king over his duties as a father. Thus, during Artaxerxes' early formative years, he had no mother or father to guide him.

Soon after becoming queen, Esther noticed Xerxes's lack of attention for the prince. She asked for the king's permission for her to take charge of the prince's upbringing. The king readily granted her request. The queen invited Mordecai and several scholars from the Great Synagogue to join the boy's Persian tutors in overseeing his education. Artaxerxes soon thrived on the attention from the queen and the mental stimulation of the scholars. But the queen was acutely aware the prince lacked friends his own age.

Even though I was her servant, the queen had made certain I received a proper education at the palace from the time of my arrival. I had an affinity for learning and excelled beyond my years in my studies.

Still, I was surprised when the queen informed me one day that she was relieving me of some of my palace duties. Instead, she wanted me to join the prince as a companion and fellow student. He was a few years older than I was, and at first it was awkward – for both of us. Neither of us knew just how to interact with the other. He would one day be the king of Persia . . . and I would always be a eunuch and a servant.

But as time passed, the prince began to recognize my intellectual prowess – I often grasped our lessons much quicker than he did. But there was no question he was the more gifted athlete. I was awkward and hesitant; he was skilled and confident.

We soon learned what the queen had known all along – we could help one another grow in our areas of weakness. Soon, we began to bond as we became one another's encourager and challenger. Though neither of us ever lost sight that he would one day be my king, we were both grateful to spend time with someone closer to our own age.

To some extent, I began to see the world through his eyes as a Persian prince; he, through my eyes as a Jew. He was curious to learn more about what we believed – more than likely not only due to my influence, but also that of the queen and Mordecai.

Our days continued that way for almost seven years. Though we always knew it would end, I was not prepared for the abruptness with which it occurred – but then again, neither was the rest of the empire. Early one morning, a cry went out throughout the palace – King Xerxes had been assassinated!

The act had been carried out by Artabanus, the commander of the royal bodyguard – one of the most powerful of Xerxes's officials. Apparently, his plan was to make himself king. Mordecai acted quickly and placed the prince under the protection of guards known to be loyal to Xerxes. Artabanus and his co-conspirators were quickly apprehended and put to death.

King Artaxerxes ascended the throne and led the kingdom in a month-long period of mourning over his father's death. I did not see him in person during that time. Then one day soon after the period of mourning concluded, one of the king's attendants appeared before me and said, "You have been summoned by the king."

7

AN UNEXPECTED HONOR

~

*A*s I entered the king's inner court, I saw Artaxerxes sitting on the throne. He looked as if he had aged at least ten years since I last saw him. His sorrow over his father's death, as well as the weight of responsibility suddenly thrust upon him, had taken their toll.

I knew Artaxerxes would always strive to be the best king possible. The welfare and safety of his people – both Persian and Jew – would always be paramount in his mind. But as I watched my burdened friend, I was overcome with compassion. I wanted to help him any way I could. But I had no idea that he was about to tell me how I could best do that.

As I bowed before my king, he motioned for me to approach. As I did, he announced, "Be it known throughout the empire that the king's cupbearer approaches. From this moment forward, nothing will be placed on my table or in my cup that Nehemiah has not approved. He has proven that he is the most trustworthy person for this position. I am placing the king's life and safety in his hands. As such, he will be recognized and honored by every official and servant within the court and throughout the empire."

I bowed even lower before my king. I knew this was a great honor, and I was humbled by his trust in me. Few in the kingdom would have greater authority than I did. And no one, including the prime minister, would have greater access to the king.

"Rise, Nehemiah," Artaxerxes declared, "as my attendants place a royal robe over your shoulders and a royal turban upon your head to signify your station. Your personal lodgings are already being arranged in the palace so you will be in close proximity to me at all times. The prime minister will provide further instruction on your duties."

"May I speak, my king?" I asked.

"You may."

"I am greatly honored by the trust you are placing in me, my king. As the God of Abraham, Isaac, and Jacob is my witness, I will serve you to the best of my ability until my last breath. May God, by His mercy and strength, protect you and grant you His favor in all that you do."

I withdrew from the king's presence to seek out Mordecai. I had seen the cupbearer who served King Xerxes many times, but I did not know the full extent of what those duties entailed. After Mordecai had given me a thorough explanation and introduced me to the kitchen staff, I asked for a moment alone with him.

"Mordecai, what happened to the previous cupbearer, and why did the king select me to serve him in this way?" I asked.

"The previous cupbearer served King Xerxes faithfully for many years," Mordecai replied. "There is a bond that develops between a king and his cupbearer that is unlike any other. The king is literally trusting his cupbearer with his life, and the cupbearer has committed to lay down his life for his king.

"The cupbearer will not only be present for public occasions but also for private gatherings. He must never let his guard down. Since the cupbearer will hear the king's private conversations, he must maintain the highest confidentiality. He often becomes the king's confidant. That is a lifelong bond. It is not simply a position of service; it is a unique relationship.

"So, though the previous cupbearer enjoyed that kind of relationship with King Xerxes, it is not a connection that is easily transferred from one king to another. Artaxerxes needs someone in that role he already trusts. He needs someone in whom he already has confidence. And that person is you, Nehemiah.

"Unlike the many other men who will surround Artaxerxes as his officials – including his prime minister, I might add – the role of cupbearer is often the most difficult position for a king to fill. But in this case, Artaxerxes never had any question. I will tell you what I once said to Queen Esther: Who can say but that God has elevated you to this position for such a time as this? Honor your king, but never forget the One you must honor above all others."

I was not prepared for the honor my new position afforded me in the city and the empire. Many of the king's officials began to treat me as a peer instead of as a servant. Most of the servants began to bow before me – an action that made me uncomfortable. I still considered myself one of them, even though I knew my position gave me certain authority over them.

The honor that surprised me most, however, was when Mordecai mentioned I was being invited to become part of the assembly of the Great

Synagogue. I had looked up to Mordecai and several of the scholars when they tutored Artaxerxes and me, but I never expected to join them in their great work.

Mordecai first introduced me to a scribe and priest named Ezra. He was considered one of the greatest living scholars of the Torah. Mordecai explained that the other scholars turned to Ezra when they had questions about certain passages in the Torah. Because of the great respect in which he was held, I was rather surprised to discover he was the youngest of the scholars – even younger than I am.

It didn't take long for me to ascertain why he was held in such esteem. As our time together unfolded, he revealed his hope and passion. "Nehemiah, I believe Jehovah God is leading me go to Jerusalem to finish the work in the Temple.

"My role would have little to do with the building itself – Zerubbabel is quite capably managing that. Rather, I believe God is calling me to restore the teaching of the Word of God in the Temple, renew the feasts commanded by God, and restore true worship.

"I have prayed for Jehovah God to grant me favor in the eyes of the king so he would permit me to travel to Jerusalem for this purpose. Do you believe the king would look favorably upon my request?"

8

IN GOD'S TIME

∾

"Queen Esther and Prime Minister Mordecai have both entreated me to send the priest Ezra to Jerusalem to complete the work begun by Zerubbabel," the king said. I had learned that he would often speak out loud in my presence to process his thoughts. I had also learned to refrain from responding unless he specifically addressed me. So I continued to listen silently.

"We have already sent a fair contingent of people, as well as significant resources, to rebuild the Temple. Why should I send more when our treasury is already being depleted by my campaign against the Greeks? My strategy to weaken the Athenians by funding their enemies is proving successful. Why would I take funds needed to conquer their empire and use them to finance the rebuilding of an empire we have already conquered?

"What's more, today I received a letter from Chancellor Rehum, written by his scribe Shimshai: [1]

To King Artaxerxes,

The king should know that the Jews who came here to Jerusalem from Babylon are rebuilding this rebellious and evil city. They have already laid the foundation and will soon finish its walls. And the king should know that if this city is rebuilt and its walls are completed, it will be much to your disadvantage, for the Jews will then refuse to pay their tribute, customs, and tolls to you.

Since we are your loyal subjects and do not want to see the king dishonored in this way, we have sent the king this information. We suggest that a search be made in your ancestors' records, where you will discover what a rebellious city this has been in the past. In fact, it was destroyed because of its long and troublesome history of revolt against the kings and countries who controlled it.

We declare to the king that if this city is rebuilt and its walls are completed, the province west of the Euphrates River will be lost to you.

From your loyal subjects in the province west of the Euphrates River –
Rehum, Shimshai, Bishlam, Mithredath, and Tabeel.

"Though I don't know the latter three men," the king continued, "I know Rehum to be a loyal subject and a capable chancellor. Our records have been searched, and they speak the truth. The Jewish people have a history of rebellion against their conquering rulers. I cannot ignore this warning and counsel, even though it is contrary to what my trusted counselor Mordecai and Queen Esther have advised. It would be more prudent to stop the work so I may investigate the accusation thoroughly than it would to send more people and resources.

"Nehemiah, call for my scribe."

My heart sank as I heard the king dictate his reply: [2]

To Rehum the governor, Shimshai the court secretary, and their colleagues living in Samaria and throughout the province west of the Euphrates River. Greetings.

The letter you sent has been translated and read to me.

I ordered a search of the records and have found that Jerusalem has indeed been a hotbed of insurrection against many kings. In fact, rebellion and revolt are normal there! Powerful kings have ruled over Jerusalem and the entire province west of the Euphrates River, receiving tribute, customs, and tolls.

Therefore, issue orders to have these men stop their work. That city must not be rebuilt except at my express command.

Be diligent, and do not neglect this matter, for you must not permit the situation to harm the king's interests.

From King Artaxerxes, King of Persia and King of Kings

Now Ezra would not be going to Jerusalem, and worse, work would be stopped upon receipt of the letter. Mordecai approached me a few days later. "The king has written to halt the work on the Temple in Jerusalem." I listened without responding, because I could not betray the king's confidence, even to Mordecai.

"Are you able to speak with him and convince him to resume the work?" Mordecai asked.

"The king is a fair man," I replied. "If he is provided with evidence that the rebuilding of the Temple is not a precursor to rebellion, I believe he would reconsider his decision. But you must produce such evidence."

Try as he might, Mordecai was unable to change the king's mind. However, in the seventh year of his reign, the king awoke one morning in great distress. "I have had a dream that troubles me," he said – again not seeking a response from me.

"I dreamed that the House of the God of the Jews lay in ruins. There was nowhere for His Spirit to dwell. Jehovah God said He was appointing me to rebuild His house, otherwise He would turn His wrath on me and my kingdom. He told me He has chosen someone to finish the work; I must send him and provide him with everything needed to complete the work.

"I do not need anyone to interpret this dream. The message is clear, and I know what I must do. Nehemiah, send for the one called Ezra!"

No one looked more surprised than Mordecai when Ezra was brought into the hall with all the king's court officials present.

The king declared, "Be it so ordered that Ezra the priest is to take as many Israelites as he needs to Jerusalem to finish rebuilding the Temple. He is to be given all the gold and silver required to restore the Temple to its original glory. In addition, it will be unlawful for anyone to levy any taxes on the Jewish priests or any others serving in the Temple.

"The work is to be completed and worship restored with all haste, and anyone who attempts to interrupt the work will answer to me!"

9

THIRTEEN YEARS

∿

*A*fter Ezra arrived in Jerusalem, he routinely sent progress reports to the king and to the Great Synagogue. The updates to the Great Synagogue always included a description of the people's spiritual condition.

"To my dismay, I have discovered the spiritual climate of the majority of our people is even worse than I was led to believe," Ezra wrote. "It is tepid at best, if not antagonistic toward anything having to do with Jehovah God. Hordes of our men have married non-Jewish women and adopted the beliefs of their wives' culture.

"Animosity quickly developed between those of us who recently arrived from Susa and those whose families never left Jerusalem, as well as the larger number of those who returned twenty years ago and have settled into this way of life." Since I knew my father and brothers were a part of the latter group, I feared that they, too, had abandoned Jehovah God and strayed from His ways.

"An earnest despair has arisen in my heart that I am unable to hide," Ezra said in a subsequent letter. "Yesterday, I could not help but tear my clothes and fall to my knees in the middle of the road as an expression of my grief over the sins of God's people. The Spirit of Jehovah God led me to call out the sins of the people with a heart cry for them to repent."

I had always been proud of my heritage and, despite my grief over my father's abandonment of me, I was grateful he was willing to return to our land to rebuild it. But I had never witnessed the deep conviction that Ezra was demonstrating toward Jehovah God. That day, a passion to love God wholeheartedly and obey Him faithfully was birthed in my heart. I desired to serve Him as earnestly as what I was witnessing in Ezra's life through his letters.

As the months passed, Ezra reported he was determined to restore the Temple and purify the community in Jerusalem from the immoral customs of the land. He continued to demonstrate his obedience to the law of God and to teach those laws to the people. He braved the opposition – some days ending in victory, other days in defeat.

Over the years, the king became greatly distracted by the revolt taking place in Egypt. King Darius, Artaxerxes's grandfather, had conquered Egypt. Darius was seen by the Egyptian people as a pharaoh, and the kingdom had prospered under his rule. But Xerxes, Artaxerxes's father, had treated the people cruelly, causing the embers of turmoil and rebellion to ignite.

Soon after Artaxerxes had assumed the throne, an Egyptian named Inaros rallied a rebel force and led them in revolt against the Persians. He succeeded in creating an alliance with the Athenians under the age-old premise that "my enemy's enemy is my friend." The revolt lasted six years before Inaros was captured and brought to Susa for execution.

Once the revolt was put down, Artaxerxes – who in many ways was more like his grandfather than his father – ruled Egypt with a more open hand, but the prosperity he sought for the region continued to elude him. Despite that, he felt he needed to concentrate on bringing closure to the long-standing conflict with the Athenians. He was somewhat successful in that effort, but the resulting peace treaty between the two empires remained tenuous.

Throughout all of this, the bond between my king and me continued to grow. There were many long days and sleepless nights I sat in his private chamber as he wrestled through decisions he needed to make. Again, I knew my position; I never offered him counsel. He had plenty of officials who did that. My role was to encourage him and assure him the right decision would become clear at the appropriate time. And by God's grace, it always did.

I would never presume to say our relationship developed into a friendship. But I will admit that for a significant season in my life, ours was the closest to a friendship I would ever have. Throughout my service to him, I was more preoccupied with my concerns for the king and his deliberations than I was for my own people or what was happening in Jerusalem.

In the months leading up to the twentieth anniversary of the king's reign, he traveled throughout the eastern portion of the empire and received the honor and accolades he was due from his people. For the first time in over 130 years, Persia was at peace. The empire was prospering, and all roads appeared to lead to Susa.

As I traveled with him, I reflected back on all that had transpired during Artaxerxes's first twenty years. Though much had changed and much had been accomplished, sometimes it felt as if it were only a moment in time.

The king decided to conclude his travels with a weeklong recreational hunt. He confided that he was going to forget about ruling the empire, and simply enjoy the hunt. He invited me to join in the sport; for that week, it felt like the days we had spent together growing up.

I had never been the marksman he was. That week he patiently tried to teach me how to improve my skills, just as he had many years earlier. To his exasperation – and to my regret – his efforts did not yield any better results this time around. It was solely his hunting prowess that provided game for us. Left to my devices, we would have gone hungry that week!

It was an enjoyable time, and we were both able to laugh. For one week, he was not the king, and I was not the cupbearer. He wasn't preoccupied with affairs of state, and I was not thinking about the condition of my people. We were simply two friends hunting together.

Little did I know what would await me the day after we returned to the palace. Little did I know I would receive a visitor who would bring the condition of our people to the forefront of my mind and heart. Little did I know I would be face to face with my brother, Hanani. And little did I know how much my life was about to change.

~

10

A GREAT BURDEN

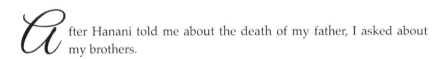

*A*fter Hanani told me about the death of my father, I asked about my brothers.

"Each of them is in good health and continues to labor on rebuilding the Temple and the city," he replied. "All four of us have married Canaanite women whose families live in neighboring villages. However, unlike most of the men in Jerusalem who have married non-Jewish women, we have not turned to the Canaanite gods. We have remained faithful to Jehovah God, and our wives have turned to Him as well.

"God has blessed each of us with sons and daughters. Our father was grandfather to sixteen grandchildren and a great-grandfather to twelve. My oldest, a son, is now thirty-two, and my youngest, a daughter, is sixteen and soon to be married. My wife and I have six grandchildren. How about you, Nehemiah, have you married?"

"No," I answered, "the opportunity to marry was taken from me when I came to live in the palace."

Hanani was startled by my statement, so I explained the conditions under which a male can serve in the household of the queen. When I finished, he looked down and said, "Nehemiah, I am so sorry. None of us knew. And I am certain our father didn't know. I don't believe he would have left you here if he had been aware. He left you here because he truly believed it was the safest place for you to grow up.

"And concerning the conditions in Jerusalem, he was correct. From the day we arrived, we were frequently attacked by marauders and men from neighboring villages who did not want to see the city rebuilt. We still live under that continuous threat."

"But is there no defense against their threats?" I asked. "Is the city wall not able to ward off their attacks?"

To my horror, he replied, "Nehemiah, there is no wall. It was torn down over 140 years ago by Nebuchadnezzar when he conquered the city. The gates also were burned, and we have never been permitted to rebuild them. We have been given permission to restore the Temple and some of the buildings, but we are still a conquered people. We are not allowed to have a defensive wall and gates to secure our city!"

I sat down and wept for my family and the distress I heard in my brother's voice. I wept over the conditions in which they were being forced to live. Through the years, I had heard about some of the opposition they faced while trying to rebuild the Temple. But I never knew my king had not let them rebuild a defensive wall.

I recently had read about the beauty of Jerusalem and the magnificence of the Temple during the days of King Solomon's reign. And I had pictured that it was again rising out of the dust as a city of splendor and a testimony to our God. But hearing that it was still a city in ruin, I wept over the dishonor it was to our God. Here I stood in the grandeur of the fortress of Susa – a testimony to the majesty of my king. Yet the city that was to be a testimony to the majesty of Jehovah God was in complete disarray.

Seeing my distress, Hanani asked, "Nehemiah, is there anything you can do? Has God placed you in this position to serve the king, at great cost to yourself, so you might enable His city to be rebuilt?"

"I do not know, Hanani," I replied. "But I will petition our God and ask what He would have me do to relieve this burden He has placed upon my heart. Join me in praying for clarity and favor. As you return to Jerusalem, ask our brothers to do the same."

I began to pray:

"O Lord, God of heaven, the great and awesome God who keeps His covenant of unfailing love with those who love Him and obey His commands, listen to my prayer! Look down and see me praying for Your people Israel. I confess that we have sinned against You. Yes, even my own family and I have sinned! We have sinned terribly by not obeying the commands, decrees, and regulations that You gave us through Your servant Moses.

"Please remember what You told Your servant Moses: 'If you are unfaithful to Me, I will scatter you among the nations. But if you return to Me and obey My commands and live by them, then even if you are exiled to the ends of the earth, I will bring you back to the place I have chosen for My name to be honored.'

"The people You rescued by Your great power and strong hand are Your servants. O Lord, please hear my prayer! Listen to the prayers of those of us who delight in honoring You. Please grant me success by making the king favorable to me. Put it into his heart to be kind to me."[1]

For days I mourned, fasted, and prayed. The days turned into weeks, and the weeks into months. It was not until the following spring, in the month of Nisan, that Jehovah God opened the door for me to have that conversation with Artaxerxes.

Apparently, I was unable to hide my distress that day. I was surprised when the king asked, "Nehemiah, *why are you so sad? You aren't sick, are you? You look like a man with deep troubles?*"[2]

I wasn't quite sure how to reply, but suddenly these words came out of my mouth: "*Long live the king! Why shouldn't I be sad? For the city where my ancestors are buried is in ruins, and the gates have been burned down.*"[3]

I had now known this king for almost thirty years and had been serving him for twenty. Not once had I ever spoken to him like that! He knew I was a Jew, but I had rarely mentioned it unless he asked me a question about certain aspects of being Jewish. I had never expressed a burden for my people . . . until that moment.

Now I stood in silence awaiting my king's response.

~

11

IF IT PLEASE THE KING

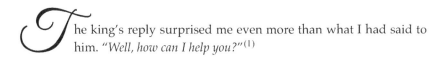

$\mathscr{T}$he king's reply surprised me even more than what I had said to him. *"Well, how can I help you?"*[1]

God gave me the words as I nervously responded, *"If it please the king, and if you are pleased with me, your servant, send me to Judah to rebuild the city where my ancestors are buried."*[2]

"How long will you be gone?" he asked. *"When will you return?"*[3]

"I do not know how long it will take to rebuild the city," I replied. "Your grandfather sent Zerubbabel seventy-five years ago to undertake the work, and Ezra has now been there thirteen years. And still, the work has not yet been completed. But if the king would permit me to go for three years, I will endeavor to finish the work in a way that honors Jehovah God and honors you and the decree you issued to have the work completed."

The king's agreement to my request gave me increased boldness, so I continued. *"If it please the king, let me have letters addressed to the governors of the provinces west of the Euphrates River, instructing them to let me travel safely through their territories on my way to Judah.*[(4)] My king knows that those governors have attempted to thwart the work since it was first begun. Letters containing your royal seal will reinforce that this work is proceeding according to your decree."

Hearing no objection from the king, I proceeded. *"And please send a letter to Asaph, the manager of your forest, instructing him to give me timber. I will need it to make beams for the gates of the Temple fortress, for the city walls, and for a house for myself."*[(5)]

By the gracious hand of God, the king not only granted my requests, but he also commanded that a contingent of army officers and horsemen travel with me for protection and remain with me throughout the work.

The king charged me with selecting someone to carry out my responsibilities as cupbearer during my absence. I already had a young man named Izak in mind, who had entered into the king's service ten years earlier. Throughout that time, he had proven to be a loyal, diligent, and trustworthy servant. I had witnessed a rapport developing between him and the king. Artaxerxes heartily accepted my recommendation.

It took three weeks to make the necessary arrangements for my departure. Our caravan set out on the first day of the month of Iyar and was met thirty days later by the Governor of Cunaxa on the western shores of the Euphrates. He, as well as governors of the other provinces we passed through, was not receptive to the reason for our expedition. They were deeply resentful of my people, dating back for many generations, and had absolutely no interest in seeing Jerusalem rebuilt. But they were men under authority and subjects of King Artaxerxes. So once I presented my letters bearing the king's royal seal, and they recognized I was being accompanied by the king's royal guard, they grudgingly let us pass without further delay.

It took us three months to reach Jerusalem. We arrived on the third day of the month of Tammuz. We were met by a host of people, including my brother, Hanani. It had been almost a year since I had seen him in Susa. He, along with many others, was encouraged the king had tasked me to lead the rebuilding efforts and had provided the resources needed to complete the work. Cheers went up from most of those who surrounded us.

Ezra was overjoyed to hear the news as well as receive the sacred writings sent by the Great Synagogue to help him restore obedience to the Mosaic laws. He confided that for much of his time here, he had felt as if he were on his own without any support. But now with my arrival, together with the resources and encouragement from the Great Synagogue, he was reenergized for the work that remained.

Hanani reintroduced me to my brothers, and then I met their wives and children. I was overcome with emotion. For so long, I had felt like an orphan; but now I was surrounded by family – brothers, sisters-in-law, nieces, and nephews. It would take me some time to learn all their names!

But not everyone was pleased to see me. I was approached by two men later that day. The first was a Horonite named Sanballat. I knew he was governor of the province of Samaria. His ancestors had never been relocated to Babylon, so he had grown up in the hills of Samaria.

Once he was of age, he was pressed into service on the garrison force in Shechem; he quickly rose to the rank of commander. Ten years before I arrived in Jerusalem, his Persian overseers had rewarded his loyalty by appointing him to his current station.

In an effort to unite the Samaritan people, one of his first orders of business was to convince his Persian overseers that a temple needed to be constructed within that province. The news of the efforts to rebuild the Temple in Jerusalem had infuriated the Samaritans and had escalated their hostility toward the Judahites and their Persian rulers. Sanballat knew people would welcome his leadership if he could successfully construct a temple within their borders.

He chose a site in Shechem on Mount Gerizim where both Abraham and Jacob had erected altars to worship Jehovah God. The design for the temple was based on Solomon's Temple in Jerusalem – rivaling it in size and splendor. Construction was completed within five years.

While construction was still underway, Sanballat arranged for his daughter, Nikaso, to marry a Levite named Manasseh. Manasseh came from the priestly line of Aaron, and Sanballat chose him to preside over the new temple. Everything proceeded according to his plan.

Even though Sanballat had established a temple in Samaria, he was adamant that the Temple in Jerusalem not be rebuilt. And in recent years, he had done everything possible to impede reconstruction.

The other man to approach me that day was an Ammonite by the name of Tobiah. Before Ezra arrived in Jerusalem, Tobiah had taken over the store-rooms of the Temple for his own use. He had made it clear he had no interest in relinquishing control. Over time, he and Sanballat had been drawn to one another through their mutual interest in making certain the Temple was not restored.

Neither man made any secret of his displeasure that I had come to help restore the city.

～

12

THE WORK BEGINS

~

Three days later, I quietly slipped out during the night, taking only three officers of the royal guard with me. I had not shared the plans God put on my heart with anyone, including them. We took no pack animals with us except the donkey I was riding.

We went out through the Valley Gate, past the Jackal's Well, and over to the Dung Gate to inspect the broken walls and burned gates. We then proceeded to the Fountain Gate and to the King's Pool, but my donkey wasn't able to pass through the rubble. So, instead we traveled through the Kidron Valley to assess the wall before we returned to the city through the Valley Gate.

I had not yet revealed my plans to any of the Jewish leaders, including Ezra, the priests, the nobles, the officials, or anyone else in the city administration. But now, having completed my survey, I called them together and said, *"You know very well what trouble we are in. Jerusalem lies in ruins, and its gates have been destroyed by fire. Let us rebuild the wall of Jerusalem and end this disgrace!"*[1]

Then I told them about how the gracious hand of God had been on me and about my conversation with the king. I shared how receptive he had been to my request and how he had made sure we had all the resources we needed. We were no longer to act like a defeated people, I declared. "We are the chosen people of Jehovah God. And if He is for us, no one can stand against us. Let us arise and build!"

They replied with one voice, "*Yes, let's rebuild the wall!*"[2]

News of my plan spread quickly, and I was again visited by Sanballat and Tobiah. This time, they brought a third man with them. "My name is Geshem," he said, "and I am chief of the Arab tribe that dwells in and around Jerusalem."

The three men expressed their contempt for my plan. "*What are you doing? Are you rebelling against the king?*"[3]

"I come with the full support and authorization of the king," I replied. "But even more importantly, I come with the direction of the God of heaven. And He *will help us succeed. We, His servants, will start rebuilding this wall. But you men will have no share or say in the work, because you have no legal right or historic claim in Jerusalem.*"[3]

As reconstruction began, I divided the work into sections and assigned someone to be responsible for the completion of each portion. For many sections of the wall, I assigned the work to people who lived in that specific area. I knew they would take greater care if the wall they were restoring protected their own homes!

No one was excluded from the work. Ezra, the high priest Eliashib, and other priests restored the wall to the west of the Sheep Gate on the north side of the Temple. Hanani and my other brothers worked on sections along the southwest ridge.

As people from nearby cities learned of our effort, they arrived to lend a hand. I gave them assignments as well. Men from the town of Jericho worked alongside the priests. People from Tekoa helped restore two sections of the wall – despite the fact their leaders succumbed to pressure from Sanballat and Tobiah and refused to work. Men from Mizpah also came and helped, despite their governor's opposition.

Even Uzziel, son of Harhaiah, a goldsmith by trade; and Hananiah, a manufacturer of perfumes, fortified a section of the wall together. Shallum, son of Hallohesh, the leader of a district of the city, brought his daughters to assist in the work. Initially, some of the people mocked Shallum until they saw those young women were better skilled than many of the men. In fact, they repaired one of the larger sections of the wall to the southwest corner of the city.

The people from Zanoah, led by their city leader, Hanun, repaired the Valley Gate despite Sanballat and Tobiah's many attempts to dissuade them. The group also repaired the southern wall all the way to the Dung Gate on the southeast corner of the city.

I assigned the rebuilding of the other gates to the most experienced carpenters, who laid the beams, set up the doors, and installed the bolts and bars. Though I had nothing with which to compare them, I believe these new gates were even stronger than the originals.

Malkijah, also a goldsmith, repaired the wall as far as the housing for the Temple servants and merchants, which was across from the Inspection Gate. Then he continued as far as the upper room at the corner. Other goldsmiths and merchants repaired the wall from that corner back to the Sheep Gate.

These were just a few of the men who labored day and night. I recorded a complete list of all the workers and their respective assignments in a journal, which is available for you to review.[5]

Asaph, the manager of the king's forest, provided the sturdiest timber and beams for us to use. With such wonderful resources, we never compromised on the structural integrity of the work.

When Sanballat saw our progress, he flew into a rage and mocked us. *"What does this bunch of poor, feeble Jews think they're doing?"* he cried out. *"Do they think they can build the wall in a single day by just offering a few sacrifices? Do they actually think they can make something of stones from a rubbish heap – and charred ones at that?"*[6]

Tobiah the Ammonite, who was standing beside him, shouted, *"That stone wall would collapse if even a fox walked along the top of it!"*[7]

Then I prayed, *"Hear us, our God, for we are being mocked. May their scoffing fall back on their own heads, and may they themselves become captives in a foreign land! Do not ignore their guilt. Do not blot out their sins, for they have provoked You to anger here in front of the builders."*[8]

When I finished, the two men turned and walked away in a huff.

13

DISCOURAGEMENT FROM OUTSIDE
AND INSIDE

~

*T*he people should have been encouraged by all the headway we were making on the walls. To the contrary, I observed they were becoming more discouraged as each day passed. A sorrowful song soon began to echo throughout the city:

> *"So much rubble for us to haul!*
> *Worn out and weary are we all!*
> *Will we ever finish this wall?"*[1]

When I investigated further, I discovered the source of the discouragement was not the work; rather, it was the continuous threats of attack from Sanballat, Tobiah, and Geshem. Several workers who lived near our enemies reported, "We have heard them making plans against us. They are threatening to swoop down and kill us while we are distracted by our work."

I called all the leaders together and announced, *"Don't be afraid of the enemy! Remember the Lord, who is great and glorious, and fight for your brothers, your sons, your daughters, your wives, and your homes!*[(2)]

"We will divide our workforce into two parts: half of the men will continue to work on the wall, while the other half stands guard with spears, shields, bows, and coats of armor. However, those working on the wall will also have a sword belted at their side. The officers and soldiers who accompanied me from Susa will station themselves behind the lowest parts of the wall in the exposed areas.

"The trumpeter will remain by my side to sound the alarm at any hint of danger. *When you hear the blast of the trumpet, rush to wherever it is sounding. Then our God will fight for us!*[(3)]

"Everyone living outside the wall will move inside Jerusalem, and those living in the city will provide them with lodging. With half our men always on guard, we will work from sunrise to sunset.

"And none of us – my kinsman, my servants, the soldiers from Susa, you as leaders, or I – will ever take off our clothes. We will be ready for battle at any moment and carry our weapons at all times."

The following day, Hanani approached me. "Brother, what you have done is a good thing. The people are encouraged by what you have put in place. But there is another enemy at work to defeat us. And that enemy attacks from within!"

"Of whom do you speak, Hanani?"

"Most of our people have large families," he replied. *"Our families need more food than we have to survive. Most of them have mortgaged their fields, vineyards,*

and homes to our nobles or foreigners in order to get food during the famine. Also, most of us have had to borrow money on our fields and vineyards from the nobles to pay our taxes.[(4)]

"Some of the families even had to sell their *children into slavery to the nobles just to get enough money to live. They have already sold some of their daughters, and they are helpless to do anything else, because their fields and vineyards were already mortgaged."*[(5)]

I burned with anger. I called a public meeting and commanded the nobles to appear before me. *"We are doing all we can to redeem our Jewish relatives who have had to sell themselves to pagan foreigners, but you are forcing them to enter back into slavery. How often must we redeem them?"*[(6)] The nobles had nothing to say in their defense.

So I pressed further. *"Stop this business of charging interest. Restore their fields, vineyards, olive groves, and homes to them this very day. And repay the interest you charged when you loaned them money, grain, new wine, and olive oil."*[(7)]

The nobles replied, *"We will give back everything and demand nothing more from the people. We will do as you say."*[(8)]

I gathered the priests and made the nobles and officials swear before them to do what they had just promised. I shook out the folds of my robe and said, *"If you fail to keep your promise, may God shake you like this from your homes and from your property!"*[(9)]

The whole assembly responded, "Amen," and they praised the Lord. The nobles kept their word, and suddenly I realized my edict applied to me as well. I could not profit from the people either.

From that moment forward, neither I nor any of my officials drew on the official food allowance we were entitled to receive under Persian law. The former governors, in contrast, had laid heavy burdens on the people. They demanded a daily ration of food and wine, as well as forty pieces of silver. Their officials had also taken advantage of the people. But that practice would no longer be allowed to continue.

I refused to appropriate any land, even though I was entitled. The timbers and beams I had requisitioned to build my house were redirected for use in restoring other buildings. I also devoted myself to working on a section of the wall, and I required all my servants to join me in doing the same.

I asked for nothing, even though I regularly fed 150 Jewish officials at my table, plus visitors from other lands. The provisions I paid for each day included one ox, six choice sheep or goats, and a sizeable quantity of poultry. And every ten days we needed a large supply of various wines. Yet, I refused to claim the governor's food allowance so I would not further burden the people.

I was confident Jehovah God would remember me and bless me for all I had done for this people.

Finally, the wall was completed to half its original height around the city, with no gaps remaining, because the people had worked so hard.

～

14

THE PEOPLE OF GOD

~

It was several weeks before Sanballat and Geshem learned we had completed rebuilding the wall to its full height, though we still had not yet hung the doors in the gates. They sent me the following message:

> Congratulations, Governor Nehemiah, on the completion of your work!
>
> Please come join us in the village of Kephirim in the plain of Ono so we might enter into a treaty with one another.

I sent my reply back with their messenger:[1]

> I am doing a great work! I cannot stop to come and meet with you.

Four more times they sent the same message, and each time I gave the same reply. On his sixth trip to see me, Sanballat's messenger arrived with this letter in hand:[2]

> To Governor Nehemiah of Judah
>
> There is a rumor among the surrounding nations, and Geshem tells me it is true, that you and the Jews are planning to rebel and that is why you are building the wall. According to his reports, you plan to be their king. He also reports that you have appointed prophets in Jerusalem to proclaim about you, 'Look! There is a king in Judah!'
>
> You can be very sure that this report will get back to the king, so I suggest that you come and talk it over with me.
>
> From The Honorable Governor Sanballat of Samaria

I replied:[3]

> You know you are lying! There is no truth in any part of your story. You are making up the whole thing.

They were trying to intimidate us, imagining they could discourage us into stopping the work. Instead, we became even more determined to rebuild the city.

A few days later, the prophet Shemaiah sent a message requesting I come see him on an urgent matter. His infirmities had prevented him from helping with the work on the wall; he was primarily confined to his home. Out of respect for him and his position, I accepted his invitation.

As soon as I arrived at his home, Shemaiah warned me I was in danger. I wanted to tell him there was nothing prophetic about that concern – my life had been in danger ever since I arrived in Jerusalem. However, I held my tongue. He continued, *"Let us meet together inside the Temple of God and bolt the doors shut. Your enemies are coming to kill you tonight."*[4]

I immediately knew his words were not from the Lord; rather, he was telling me to do something God had expressly forbidden. No one, other than the high priest, is permitted to enter that portion of the Temple. It was obvious Tobiah and Sanballat were manipulating Shemaiah. They hoped to intimidate me so I would heed the prophet's counsel and commit a sin against God. Then they could accuse and discredit me.

"Should someone in my position run from danger?" I asked. *"Should someone in my position enter the Temple to save his life?* Should I defile the Temple and disobey my God by doing that which He has commanded only the high priest do? *No, I won't do it!"*[5]

Attempts to intimidate me continued from all quarters. Numerous letters went back and forth between Tobiah and the nobles of Judah. I learned that many in Judah had sworn allegiance to Tobiah because of his father-in-law, Shecaniah – one of the priests who had accompanied Zerubbabel back to the city. Tobiah's son Jehohanan was married to the daughter of Meshullam, who had shown his dedication to God and the work by rebuilding two sections of the wall.

Numerous people told me about Tobiah's good deeds, and that I had the wrong impression of him. They tried to convince me through his associations and his deeds that he was trustworthy. But most of those same people were quick to report to him every change in our plans. They told him everything I said right up until the day the wall was finished.

We completed the wall on the seventeenth day of Tishrei, just fifty-two days after the work had begun. Our enemies and surrounding nations were frightened and humiliated when they heard the news. They realized this work had been done with the help of our God.

But the completion of the wall was only the beginning of the work. The next step was to establish leadership over the city by men who loved God – honorable men who were trustworthy. Sadly, I realized that only a few in the city met those qualifications.

One of those was my brother, Hanani, and another was Hananiah, who had traveled with me from Susa. I named Hanani the governor of the city. Throughout my time in Jerusalem, he had proven he was a capable leader who was well respected. I assigned Hananiah the position of commander of the fortress. Not only was he a well-trained soldier and capable officer, but he was also a faithful man who feared God more than most.

"The gates of Jerusalem are not to be opened until the sun is hot, and they are to be closed and bolted before the sun falls behind the surrounding hills," I instructed them. "Appoint guards from those who live inside the walls of Jerusalem. They will have the greatest commitment to keeping the gates secure since they will be protecting their own homes and families. Give each of them a post in front of his own house.[6]

"The city is large and spacious, but the population living inside its walls is small since most of the houses have not yet been rebuilt. For too long, the people have lived here as exiles, devoid of identity and solidarity. Call together all the men of the city and have them register according to their genealogy so their family identity is reestablished.

"Start with family members of those who returned to Jerusalem with Zerubbabel. Give them an opportunity to celebrate the faithfulness of their ancestors who, at great risk, returned to reestablish their city and their land. Remind them all of their position as a chosen people. Remind them of God's faithfulness throughout the centuries. And remind them of God's providence and love as we reassemble in this place He gave our ancestors over 1,000 years ago.

"We are no longer exiles. We are the people of Jehovah God!"

15

THE LAW REVEALED

～

*T*he following week, I summoned all the men, women, and children (who were old enough to understand) to assemble in the square inside the Water Gate. I directed Ezra to read from the Book of the Law. He stood on a high wooden platform, reading from early morning until noon.

As Ezra read, the people began to weep as they fell under conviction. No one needed to tell them they had drifted away from their God and the laws He had given them.

Ezra and I became acutely aware we needed to explain the laws to the people since many did not know our history. Ezra began to read one section at a time so he or I could then interpret the readings for them.

Gradually the people began to lift their hands toward heaven chanting, *"Amen! Amen!"*[1]

One by one they bowed and worshiped the Lord. After a while, I stood up and declared, *"Today is a sacred day before the Lord your God.*[(2)] Rejoice in all the Lord your God has accomplished through you. Celebrate His good works with your sons and daughters.

"Go and celebrate with a feast of choice foods and sweet drinks, and share your food with people who have nothing prepared. This is not a day for sadness, for the joy of the Lord is your strength!"[(3)]

So the people left for their respective sections of the city to eat and drink, to share gifts of food with one another, and to celebrate the words of the Lord they now understood.

The following day, family leaders, priests, and Levites met with Ezra to better understand the law in further detail. As they studied, they discovered the Lord had commanded through Moses that those very days be set aside as the Festival of Shelters. The festival had been instituted by God to commemorate the Exodus and the people's journey to the land of His promise.

An important part of the celebration was the construction of temporary shelters, similar to those the people lived in during the Exodus. "Go to the hills to get branches from olive, wild olive, myrtle, palm, and fig trees," I exhorted. "Use the branches to make shelters where you will lodge throughout the festival."[(4)]

The people built shelters on the roofs of their homes, in their courtyards, in the squares inside the gates, or in the courtyards of God's Temple. For seven days we lodged in those shelters, and each day Ezra stood on the platform inside the Water Gate and read to us from the Book of the Law.

Ezra noted that our people had not observed this festival since the days of Joshua, son of Nun. On the thirtieth day of Tishrei, the final day of the festival, I declared no work was to be done as we gathered for a solemn closing assembly of fasting and prayer.

Sixteen days later, Ezra and I brought the people back together. However, this gathering was only for those of Israelite descent. Because this time we were doing so – not as a remembrance of God's gracious work on behalf of our people in days past – but as a time of confession of our own sins and those of our ancestors. Ezra called upon us to fast, dress in burlap cloth, and sprinkle dust on our heads.

For three hours, he read from the Book of the Law before directing us to observe a time of confession and worship. Several of the Levite leaders stood up and shouted, *"Stand up and praise the Lord your God, for He lives from everlasting to everlasting. Praise His glorious name! It is far greater than we can think or say."*[5]

The Levite leaders recounted the goodness and graciousness of God from the days of Abraham through His deliverance into the promised land – and from the days of the judges through those of the kings. The Levites reminded us that, despite the faithfulness of our God, time and again our people had rebelled against Him. Our people had turned to false gods, rejected God's prophets, and committed terrible blasphemies.

The Levites cried out, *"But in their time of trouble, the people called out to You, O God, and You heard from Your heaven and sent them deliverers who rescued them from their enemies. However, when all was going well, Your people turned to sin again, once more You allowed their enemies to conquer Your people.*[6]

"But in Your great mercy, You did not destroy them completely or abandon them forever. What a gracious and merciful God You are![7]

"So now today we are slaves in the land of plenty that You gave our ancestors for their enjoyment! We are slaves here in this good land. The lush produce of this

land piles up in the hands of the kings whom You have set over us because of our
sins. They have power over us and our livestock. We serve them at their pleasure,
and we are in great misery. [8]

"Because of all this, O merciful God, we are making a solemn promise and putting
it in writing, to honor You, obey Your Law, and not neglect Your Temple.
On this sealed document are the names of our leaders and Levites and priests." [9]

My signature was at the top of the document, followed by Ezra's. Other
signees included twenty-two of the leading priests, seventeen Levites, and
forty-four nobles and leaders, including all four of my brothers and
Hananiah.

Then the rest of the people – the priests, the Levites, the gatekeepers, the
singers, the Temple servants, and all who had separated themselves from
the pagan people of the land in obedience to the Law of God – followed
their leaders and bound themselves with an oath. They were joined by
their wives, sons, daughters, and all who were old enough to understand.
They swore a curse on themselves if they failed to obey the Law of God as
issued by His servant Moses.

16

DEDICATION OF THE WALL

~

a s I prepared for the dedication of the new wall, I sent word to all the Levites throughout the land to come to Jerusalem to assist in the ceremonies. They would offer songs of thanksgiving and the music of cymbals, harps, and lyres. The priests and Levites first purified themselves; then they purified the people, the gates, and the wall.

I assembled singers from the region surrounding Jerusalem. I led the leaders of Judah to the top of the wall and organized two large choirs to give thanks. One of the choirs proceeded southward along the top of the wall to the Dung Gate.

The second choir went northward past the Tower of the Ovens to the Broad Wall, past the Ephraim Gate to the Old City Gate, past the Fish Gate and the Tower of Hananel, and on to the Tower of the Hundred. Then we continued on to the Sheep Gate and stopped at the Guard Gate.

From there, both choirs traveled to the Temple of God, where they took their places on either side of me, along with the group of leaders.

Ezra led a procession of priests who played trumpets, together with those who used the musical instruments prescribed by King David, the man of God. At the Fountain Gate, they climbed the steps where the wall inclined toward the City of David. They passed the house of David and the Water Gate on the east before arriving at the Temple.

Women and children also participated in the joyous celebration, which could be heard far away. As I watched the festivities, I thought about the day I arrived in Jerusalem less than four months earlier. The physical signs of defeat and despair were gone; the city had been physically transformed.

But beyond that, the city had been spiritually transformed. The spirit of oppression I had witnessed was replaced by a spirit of joy and confidence. God had transformed all our lives – mine included. The restored wall was but a symbol of our revival.

I appointed several men to be in charge of the storerooms for the offerings, the first part of the harvest, and the tithes. Tobiah had long since vacated those rooms, and his remaining possessions were removed before the rooms were purified.

These men were responsible for collecting portions for the priests and Levites, as required by law, from fields outside the towns. Since their service was in obedience to God, the people of Judah took joy in providing for their needs.

The singers and gatekeepers also provided a great service to the people. The custom of having choir directors lead choirs in hymns of praise and thanksgiving to God began during the days of David. It was only appropriate that all Israel bring a daily supply of food for the singers, the gatekeepers, and the Levites. The Levites, in turn, gave a portion of what they received to the priests, the descendants of Aaron.

With so much of the work now completed, Ezra and I decided the assembly of the Great Synagogue needed to be relocated to Jerusalem. We would continue the work that had begun in Susa. It was fitting that the safeguarding of Scripture, the teachings regarding the holy feasts, and the recording of the Oral Law be done here. I sent word to Mordecai expressing our conviction. I assured him the priests and Levites already in Jerusalem were capable of continuing the work.

I was relieved when he replied:

> To Nehemiah, Governor of Judah,
> and Ezra, the scribe,
>
> The other scribes and scholars here in Susa agree with me that the knowledge of the Great Synagogue should be housed in Jerusalem. I will arrange for the safe transport of all the materials amassed here under protection of the royal guard. May God continue to bless you both in all that He has accomplished through the two of you.
>
> Your humble servant,
> Mordecai, Prime Minister of Persia

Three months later, the materials arrived and were stored in the building we had already prepared. Though I was overjoyed by their arrival, Ezra had mixed emotions – joy, awe, gratitude, and humility – knowing this great treasure had now been entrusted into our care.

We immediately chose a man named Malachi, who was born in Jerusalem, to be part of the assembly. His grandfather had accompanied Zerubbabel at the beginning of the Temple restoration. Soon after Ezra arrived in the city, he had begun mentoring Malachi.

Malachi had proven himself to be a man dedicated to Jehovah God, His ways, and His work. Ezra and I both knew he would be a valuable contributor. Malachi would be able to concentrate all his attention on the work, while Ezra and I would need to divide our efforts with our other responsibilities.

I was never more grateful for Malachi than when my friend and confidant, Ezra, died several months later. My heart ached, but as governor, I needed to help our people grieve their loss. My grief would need to wait.

We mourned Ezra's death for thirty days. But, for many of us, it took much longer to get over the hole left in our hearts. Our people began to look to me, not only to be their governor, but also to shepherd them in the ways of the Lord. Though the priests in the Temple carried out their sacred duties, it was I who became their spiritual leader.

A familiar prayer poured out of my heart: "I am Your servant, O Lord. Please hear my prayer and grant me success as I endeavor to lead Your people through this difficult hour."

∾

17

TRANSITIONS

⁓

After the mourning period passed, I dispatched the following message to the king:

To The King of Kings, The Great King Artaxerxes of Persia,

The king graciously permitted me to come to Jerusalem on your behalf to complete the work of rebuilding the city. My three years are now drawing to a conclusion. I should be preparing to return to Susa. However, as you already know, Ezra the scribe - whom you sent to restore the Temple and the Laws of Jehovah God - has died. His death has left a significant vacancy in the leadership needed to continue the work here.

Your provision and approval have enabled Jerusalem to

be restored to a state that honors Jehovah God, as well as you and your kingdom. I fear that my immediate departure, combined with the death of Ezra, will leave an absence of leadership that could impede the progress we have made.

If it please the king, I respectfully request I be allowed to remain in Jerusalem for now to ensure the stability as work continues. I will, however, abide by whatever the king decides.

Your servant,
Nehemiah

It took five weeks for my message to arrive in Susa and another five weeks for me to receive the king's reply. In the interim, I began hearing reports that Sanballat and Tobiah were again stirring up trouble. In fact, I received the following message from them:

To Governor Nehemiah of Judah,

It has come to my attention that it is time for you to return to Susa to resume your responsibilities as the king's cupbearer. But I have been informed you are not preparing to return. Perhaps you have decided to make yourself the king of Jerusalem, as I have always suspected. I will be sending a report to King Artaxerxes to notify him of your disobedience and insolence. You would do well to leave Jerusalem quickly before he dispatches his soldiers to remove you.

From The Honorable Governor Sanballat of Samaria

I wasted no time in sending my reply:

To Governor Sanballat,

You need not concern yourself with my affairs or those of Judah - and Jerusalem specifically - as we function each day with the approval and good graces of our king. I would, however, caution you from continuing to make such baseless accusations, which will only cause the king to grow weary of your selfish ambitions. Perhaps it is you who needs to prepare to leave.

From Governor Nehemiah

Shortly thereafter, I received the following dispatch from the king:

To my servant Nehemiah, Governor of Judah,

Do not think the success of your efforts has gone unnoticed. In addition to your monthly progress updates, I have received regular reports from your enemies and your allies. They have affirmed that you were the right man to send to Jerusalem to complete the work. You have honored me in all you have done, and you have honored your God.

I could not ask for or expect any greater faithfulness to me or to the work. You have kept my interests, and those of your God, before all others. Therefore, if you tell me you need additional time to complete the work I have given you, then you shall have it.

Continue to keep me informed of your progress, and I will await your return to Susa when the time is right.

King Artaxerxes, King of Persia and King of Kings

With the king's blessing – and without further interference – I proceeded to lead the people of Judah to follow the laws of God and restore Jerusalem. However, I knew my enemies still remained in the shadows.

Not long after, I received news that Mordecai had died. As I grieved, I reminisced about my early years in the fortress in Susa, where he had been a surrogate father to me. Mordecai always watched out for me, and I could always turn to him for counsel. That role did not cease as I grew older; it only matured.

God had worked through Mordecai in his role as the king's prime minister to bring about the protection and restoration of our people and to rebuild Jerusalem. Mordecai was one of the founders of the Great Synagogue. Our people would never truly know how indebted we were to him for all he had done. But I knew . . . and I mourned his death.

I also was concerned what would happen in Susa with his passing. He had been a wise and steady voice in the ear of our king. Who would take his place? That decision would have great bearing on the work here in Judah.

King Artaxerxes appointed an army officer named Shapur to succeed Mordecai as prime minister. He was neither an advocate for the Jews nor a detractor. With Queen Esther still having great influence over the king, the transition had little impact on our work. However, the queen's death several years later raised the concern once more. Though I mourned her passing, I was even more troubled about the ramifications of her death on our people. Now there was no one with close access to the king to ensure he continued to look favorably on our people.

That is when I received this dispatch from the king:

> To my servant Nehemiah, Governor of Judah,
>
> It is time for you to return to Susa. I need you here.
>
> Make the necessary arrangements to transfer your leadership there, and make preparations for your return.
>
> Time is of the essence, so do not delay.
>
> King Artaxerxes, King of Persia and King of Kings

I named my brother Hanani as temporary governor of Judah. I knew he would lead well. However, I had less trust in the high priest Eliashib's ability to lead. But I left it in the Lord's hands and prayed He would grant both men success.

Two weeks later, I departed for Susa.

∼

18

BACK IN SUSA

~

*A*s I rode into Susa after being gone twelve years, I felt like a stranger in a foreign land. Jerusalem was my home now, and I missed it greatly. The buildings in Susa were majestic, just as I remembered them. The golden ornaments that adorned the streets shone brightly in the sun. The rich colors of the Persian tapestries and clothing revealed every color of the rainbow.

But none of it eased my sadness; only my return to Jerusalem would do that. However, I had no idea when – or even if – I would return. The king had graciously granted me a twelve year absence, but now he had summoned me home. I did not know why, but I was always mindful I served at his pleasure.

Mordecai had once reminded me from the "Proverbs of Solomon:"

"My son, fear the Lord and the king, and do not join with those who do otherwise, for disaster will arise suddenly from them, and who knows the ruin that will come from them both?"[1]

Jehovah God had used my king to grant me success. Now, He had led me to return to him, and I needed to trust my God and honor my king. I knew I could not enter into the king's presence with a sad countenance. I must honor him with gratitude and joy over what he had permitted me to do.

King Artaxerxes was meeting with a number of his officials in the king's hall, but he had instructed his guards to grant me access when I arrived. He looked up and beckoned me to approach as I entered.

Addressing his officials, he said, "Gentlemen, Governor Nehemiah has arrived at a most opportune time. He can provide us with the insight we need to make a decision." Turning back to me, he said, "Nehemiah, welcome back to the palace. You have been absent for far too long, and your king is pleased to have you back."

"My king," I replied, "as always, you are most gracious – in your words and in your actions. I, and the people of Judah, will never be able to adequately thank you for your patronage in restoring Jerusalem and all that is within it to a condition that honors you and honors the God of the Jews. You have placed a great trust in me and your Jewish subjects, and we are indebted to you."

"Nehemiah, you have honored me in the way you have conducted your-self – as my emissary and as a leader," the king declared. "You have been able to complete the work that many before you failed to do. You showed great diplomacy and strength of character in dealing with those who attempted to stand in your way. You restored not only the physical struc-ture of the city, but you also have restored the heart of the city!

"Which is why I have asked you to return to Susa. I need proven leaders like you during these critical days of our empire. The officials you see standing before me are capable, loyal, and intelligent. But none of them has your experience in leading a people who are subjects of my empire to a place beyond contentment.

"Though they are still under my rule, the people of Jerusalem have had their hearts and pride restored. We can only continue to grow as an empire if we can accomplish that same transformation with all of our conquered lands. There is strength in our varied peoples and lands coming together as a Persian empire. It is better for us all. But we must see ourselves as one empire made up of diverse people, benefitting from that diversity. Otherwise, I will be forced to rule as if I were a jailer keeping guard over my conquered prisoners."

"Your majesty," I responded, "you give me more credit than any one man is due. Whatever success I was able to achieve in Jerusalem was the result of the grace and favor extended to me by my God and the support and authority granted me by my king. The extent to which I am able to be of service to you today will be dependent on those same two factors. With the favor of the Almighty and the support of my king, I will do whatever you need me to do."

The king then explained that an uprising had recently occurred in Memphis on the western bank of the Nile River. The inner turmoil that ensued during King Xerxes's rule had not fully abated since Artaxerxes had taken the throne. The officials in the king's hall were arguing in favor of an increased military presence in Egypt to squelch all signs of rebellion.

King Artaxerxes, however, knew the people would see such an action as a return to the cruelty perpetrated by Xerxes. Though Artaxerxes had been endeavoring to return Egypt to the days of prosperity enjoyed under King Darius, he had been unsuccessful in regaining the Egyptians' trust.

I asked the king if he would grant me the opportunity to survey the situation in Egypt so I might be able to bring him a recommendation. Unlike when I had proposed a plan to him to restore the city of Jerusalem, I had very little information about the conditions in Memphis. Clearly, neither did the king's officials sitting before me.

"If it please the king," I continued, "would you also grant me a small number of your most trusted guards, dressed in plain attire, to travel with me? We would not want to appear as military spies sent in to plan for an attack. And we will remain small in number so we can travel quickly."

"This is a good plan," the king replied. "You will go as my emissary, and I will provide you with letters of introduction and authorization to present to the governor of Memphis. But first you must rest and give me a full report on all that has taken place in Jerusalem."

19

MEMPHIS

~

We pushed our horses hard, but still it took fifty days for me and the six soldiers traveling with me to pass through the Arabian desert and arrive in Memphis. The lush terrain with its majestic palm trees was a welcome respite from the arid desert.

We were dressed like traveling merchants so as not to attract attention. I had decided to survey the city before presenting myself to the governor. There were obvious signs of the recent uprising. The entire city seemed to be on edge, with the Persian guards conspicuously demonstrating their presence, and the Egyptian residents clearly showing their resentment.

Memphis had once been a great city. Though its walls and buildings had not been destroyed to the extent of Jerusalem's, it had become scarred and decayed by the annual flooding of the entire river delta. The Egyptians had built dams to control the flooding, but lack of proper maintenance under foreign rule had left the barriers ineffective. Those who now resided in Memphis appeared to have no interest in protecting a city they felt was no longer their own – and their Persian overseers had no interest in wasting tax dollars on maintaining such a tumultuous city.

I quickly realized that the residents' spirit of rebellion, though it started with Xerxes's cruelty, was fostered by Artaxerxes's perceived apathy. Though I knew it was not the king's intent, his lack of proactive invest-ment and concern for the people's welfare had left them resentful.

Once a regional center for bustling commerce and trade, Memphis's work-shops and warehouses now struggled to eke out sufficient food and merchandise to support the city – except for the tables of the Persian over-seers, which further alienated the people.

After five days of surveying the city, I made contact with the local gover-nor, a Persian by the name of Babak. Once I presented him with my letter of introduction from the king, he became very suspicious as to my reason for coming to Memphis. He considered my presence to be an intrusion. He had heard of my success in Jerusalem and suspected I had been sent by the king to replace him.

The governor's opulent fortress was in stark contrast to the needs I had witnessed throughout the city. Though Governor Babak did not seem to be uncaring about the conditions in the city, he gave no indication that he felt any responsibility for improving them. It takes a warrior to conquer a people, but it takes a leader to govern a city. Governor Babak was neither; he had simply taken on the role of caretaker – with more emphasis on "taker" than on "care."

I had now seen enough and was ready to send my report to the king:

To the King of Kings, the Great King Artaxerxes of Persia,

The situation here is much as you suspected. In the eyes of the people, the city is decaying while their Persian rulers do nothing about it. No one is leading them to make needed repairs or working to restore their failing economy. Thus, the city continues to implode with no hope for the future.

I am well aware that you desire to see this city thrive. Therefore, I recommend that action be taken similar to what you commissioned in Judah. You must first win over the Egyptians by leading them to repair the damage to the surrounding dams, so the city is protected against flooding.

My next suggestion is to authorize repairs to the river harbor so it can again flourish as a port of trade. And allow for the completion of the irrigation projects, begun under King Darius, so the fields farther inland can produce greater harvests.

At the same time, restore part of the people's income by reducing the percentage of taxes levied against them. This will provide them with the added resources needed to invest in their businesses in order to restore trade with other parts of the region. In the end, the empire will receive more taxes through the smaller percentage of a much larger economy.

And further, if it please the king, recall Governor Babak and permit your servant to assume his responsibilities until such time as I am able to train someone who can serve you well in this role.

While I am awaiting your reply, I will present Governor Babak with the letter you already provided me, authorizing me to undertake repairs to the dams with his full cooperation.

As ever, I am your servant,
Nehemiah

As you might suspect, the governor was not pleased when I presented him with the king's directive for me to preside over the repairs to the dams. I insisted Babak gather the people to announce that King Artaxerxes had become aware of the condition of the surrounding dams and had sent me to assist them in making repairs. The crowd's cheers were the first positive sound I had heard since I entered the city.

"The king has also authorized us to obtain whatever resources are needed to make the repairs," I announced. "It will not be paid for out of your pockets; rather, it will be funded from the king's treasury!" A second cheer rang out from the crowd.

"Whoever is willing to help complete the work so future flooding can be prevented, come join me over here," I continued, as I gestured toward my right. "And the more men who help, the sooner the job will be done!" A third cheer rang out as men from throughout the crowd made their way to me.

Governor Babak quietly made his way back to his fortress. It was obvious he had done all he planned to do.

❧

20

THE KING'S REPLY

❧

I divided the work into sections, much as I had in Jerusalem. Although the expanse of the dams was much greater than the wall, this time there was no one threatening opposition to the work. I quickly identified those who had skill in stone masonry. I established the sections according to their number and directed them to identify laborers from the crowd to assist them.

I also chose those with quarry experience to take charge of procuring the materials we would need. They, in turn, selected the large number of workers needed to transport the materials to the dam. By the time the afternoon was done, all of the workers had an assignment.

The next morning, the masons determined what materials were needed and began their preparations. Meanwhile, the quarry workers started mining and transporting the materials. I soon witnessed a camaraderie develop among the workers in the midst of their hard labor that began to positively influence the entire city.

There were no longer signs of rebellion, and the tension subsided. The Egyptians began to regard me, the guards who had accompanied me, and the other Persian soldiers assigned to me by the governor, as their co-laborers.

At the same time, the strain between Babak and me began to ease. He, too, saw the change taking place in the city. Rather than resenting it, he now wanted to help foster it. He soon became an ally instead of the obstacle I had thought he would be.

It took four months to complete repairs on the dams – just in time for the rainy season. As a result, we didn't need to wait long to see if our work was successful. Thankfully, the waters of the Nile were contained, and there was no longer any threat of flooding.

I encouraged Babak to open the fortress stores and provide a celebration banquet for all the workers. When the Egyptians saw what was being done, they also brought provisions for the banquet. It was a king's feast, worthy of any ruler in any land!

The following morning, the two messengers I had sent to Susa returned. They presented me with the king's response:

To my trusted servant Nehemiah, the king's minister,

I knew when I sent you to Memphis you were uniquely suited for the task. Your God has truly granted you favor and understanding in what needs to be done. Please proceed immediately with everything you have proposed. The accompanying letters will authorize the procurement of all necessary resources.

From this day forward, you are now governor of Memphis with full authority to do whatever you see fit. I am including a letter advising Governor Babak that he has been recalled.

King Artaxerxes, King of Persia and King of Kings

My first appointment after reading the letter was with Babak. "Governor, the king has authorized us to proceed with all of the work requested. We are to begin repairs on the harbor so it can reopen as a port of trade. We are to reduce the percentage of tax being levied on the people with the understanding they invest those funds in rebuilding their businesses. And we are to complete the irrigation project begun by King Darius."

Babak was as pleased as I was. I showed him the letters of authorization from the king – with the exception of one. I did not show him the letter recalling him to Susa. I now knew he was the governor I would be training, and there was no need to relieve him of his duties. I would teach him as he continued to serve – and he would be none the wiser that I had disobeyed the king's command in this one instance. And I was certain the king would not take offense to my actions.

Over the next five years, we completed the work authorized by the king. Memphis was transformed. It became a city – both physically and relationally – of which the Egyptians and the Persians could be proud. The city prospered, the people prospered, and the king prospered.

When he later learned of my decision regarding Babak, the king was surprised, but not disapproving. He had authorized me to do whatever needed to be done – and that decision had proven to be one of my best.

Babak became the governor the king needed. The king became Pharoah in the eyes of the people, and Babak became their beloved governor. Memphis had become a very different city from the one I had entered almost six years earlier. It had been restored to its former splendor and magnificence – and some might say, it now surpassed its former glory.

I had completed the work for which the king had sent me, and now it was time for me to return to Susa. But in my heart, I wanted to return to my home – Jerusalem. So you can imagine my emotions when I received the following letter from my king:

> To my trusted servant Nehemiah, the king's minister,
>
> Congratulations are in order for your most excellent work on my behalf and on behalf of the empire. You have again shown yourself to be not only my most trusted official, but also my most capable. You have done in Memphis what no other man could - and I know you will tell me it was because of the favor of your God. You are almost making me a believer in Him.
>
> You have earned a rest. It is time for you to come home to Susa to receive the accolades you are due. But I have one more assignment before you return.
>
> I have received reports that turmoil has returned to Jerusalem. I need you to follow the path of your Israelite ancestors and make your way from Egypt to Judah, where you will continue to serve as governor. The people are wandering in the absence of a leader. I need you to go on my behalf and be that leader. And may your God go with you!

King Artaxerxes, King of Persia and King of Kings

If only the king had been able to see my smile. I was going home!

21

RETURN TO JERUSALEM

~

*W*hen I arrived in Jerusalem, I discovered that many things were not as I had left them. Malachi reported how quickly our people turned back to their old ways after my departure. The high priest Eliashib had permitted his relative Tobiah to again take over a large storage room in the Temple. Instead of storing the needed offerings, spices, utensils, and tithes used in the daily function of the Temple, it had been turned back into a thief's den.

I was enraged when I learned Eliashib had done such an evil thing. I went to the storeroom with the men who had accompanied me and threw all of Tobiah's belongings out into the street. I insisted the priests purify the rooms and immediately return the items that were supposed to be there.

I then was informed the Levites had not been given what was due them for quite some time. They and the singers had all abandoned their responsibilities so they could return to working in their own fields.

I immediately confronted the leaders – including Eliashib and my brother, Hanani – and demanded, *"Why has the Temple of God been neglected?"*[1]

Not one of the men answered me; instead, they looked away in shame. I banished Eliashib from my presence and from his duties in the Temple. I also dismissed his son, Joiada, because he had married Sanballat's daughter. I installed Shelemiah as the new high priest and placed Zadok the scribe and Pedaiah the Levite over the storerooms.

I turned to my brother. "Hanani, of all people, you know how we toiled to restore the Temple to be a place of honor to the name of the Lord our God. You know the Temple has always been a reflection of how we worship Jehovah God with our hearts. Compromise in the Temple is evidence of compromise in our hearts. How could you permit this to happen?"

"Eliashib convinced me that the changes in the Temple would provide greater offerings," Hanani replied. "We are a poor people living on meager means. If we could make a change that would enable the Temple's treasury to increase, would that not honor God?"

"But, brother, at what cost?" I countered. "We must always guard against our human efforts to compromise God's Word by attempting to do His work in our way! Did you receive any income personally from Tobiah for permitting this to take place?"

My heart fell even further when Hanani replied, "Yes, but it was only a small amount to help me in meeting the needs of my family."

My grief was compounded by the fact he did not recognize the error of his ways. It was a very personal reminder to me of how easily we can become blinded by our sin against God.

With a heavy heart, I removed my brother as governor of Jerusalem, and banished him from the city. I replaced him with Hanan, son of Zaccur. All of these men – Shelemiah, Zadok, Pedaiah, and Hanan – just like Malachi, had remained faithful during my absence. I prayed they would fulfill their duties in a God-honoring way, where others had not.

I called all the Levites back to the Temple and restored them to their duties. When the people saw what I had done, they brought their tithes of grain, new wine, and olive oil so the storerooms could be refilled.

I expelled Tobiah and told him he could never return. I later learned he had traveled to Samaria. Though I initially received threats from him and Sanballat, I never saw either of them again.

On the following Sabbath, I saw men of Judah treading out their wine-presses. Some were also bringing wine, grapes, figs, and other produce into the city to sell. I also saw several men from Tyre, who lived in Jerusalem, bringing in fish and all kinds of merchandise to sell. I rebuked them all for not honoring the Sabbath and told them to remove their goods.

I sought out the nobles of Judah and confronted them. *"Why are you profaning the Sabbath in this evil way? Wasn't it just this sort of thing that your ancestors did that caused our God to bring all this trouble upon us and our city? Now you are bringing even more wrath upon Israel by permitting the Sabbath to be desecrated in this way!"*[2]

I commanded the gates of Jerusalem be shut as darkness fell every Friday evening; they were not to be opened until the Sabbath ended. I sent some of my own servants to guard the gates so no merchandise could enter the city on the Sabbath day.

Initially, several merchants and tradesmen camped outside the city gates over the Sabbath, but I reprimanded them. *"What are you doing out here, camping around the wall? If you do this again, I will arrest you!"*[(3)] That was the last time they came on the Sabbath.

After several weeks, I instructed the Levites to purify themselves and resume guarding the gates to ensure the holiness of the Sabbath was preserved.

Around the same time, I realized that a number of men of Judah had married women from Ashdod, Ammon, and Moab during my absence – despite the fact we had all vowed not to do so. Half their children were speaking the language of Ashdod, or some other people, and could not speak the language of Judah. So I challenged them, *"Your wives are from nations about which the Lord has specifically told the Israelites, 'You must not intermarry with them, because they will surely turn your hearts after their gods.'*

"Wasn't this exactly what led King Solomon of Israel into sin?" I demanded. *"There was no king from any nation who could compare to him, and God loved him and made him king over all Israel. But even he was led into sin by his foreign wives. How could you even think of committing this sinful deed and acting unfaithfully toward God by marrying women who worship false gods?"*[(5)]

I made them swear in the name of God they would not permit their children to intermarry with people who follow false gods.

Afterward, I tore my cloak and shirt, pulled out hair from my head and beard, and sat down in the street. All who trembled at the words of our God came and sat with me because of the sin allowed to continue unchecked in the city.

After a while, I got to my knees and lifted my hands to Jehovah God and prayed, *"O my God, I am utterly ashamed; I blush to lift up my face to you. For our sins are piled higher than our heads, and our guilt has reached to the heavens. From the days of our ancestors until now, we have been steeped in sin. That is why we and our kings and our priests have been at the mercy of the pagan kings of the land. We have been killed, captured, robbed, and disgraced, just as we are today.*

"But now we have been given a brief moment of grace, for You have allowed a few of us to survive as a remnant. You have given us security in this holy place. You have brightened our eyes and granted us some relief from our slavery. For we were slaves, but in Your unfailing love You did not abandon us. Instead, You caused the kings of Persia to treat us favorably. You revived us so we could rebuild Your Temple and repair its ruins. You have given us a protective wall in Judah and Jerusalem.[6]

"And now, our God – the great, mighty, and awesome God – who keeps His covenant of unfailing love, we bow before You and declare, 'We will do everything the Lord asks of us.'"

King Artaxerxes granted me permission to remain in Jerusalem, my beloved home. I never returned to Susa – and I never saw my king . . . and my friend . . . again. He died nine years ago. I grieved his death more than any other.

Three kings have now succeeded Artaxerxes. The third, his son Darius II, is currently on the throne. But he, like those before him, has never approached the stature of his father.

As for the people of Judah, did they live up to that declaration we made ten years ago – to do everything God asks of us? They did . . . for a time. But then they turned away, just like those who had gone before them . . . and just like those who have come after them.

～

PLEASE HELP ME BY LEAVING A REVIEW!

i would be very grateful if you would leave a review of this book. Your feedback will be helpful to me in my future writing endeavors and will also assist others as they consider picking up a copy of the book.

To leave a review:

Go to: amazon.com/dp/1956866205

Or scan this QR code using your camera on your smartphone:

Thanks for your help!

~

COMING THIS FALL 2023

the first book in **The Parables** series

An Elusive Pursuit

*A Young Man's Journey
To Discover His Dream*

Twenty-three year old R. Eugene Fearsithe boarded a train on the first day of April 1912 in pursuit of his elusive dream. Little did he know where the journey would take him, or what . . . and who . . . he would discover along the way.

For more information, go to kenwinter.org/an-elusive-pursuit

Or scan this QR code using your camera on your smartphone

NOW AVAILABLE IN AUDIO!

The Called series is now available as audiobooks.

A Carpenter Called Joseph (Book 1)

A Prophet Called Isaiah (Book 2)

A Teacher Called Nicodemus (Book 3)

A Judge Called Deborah (Book 4)

A Merchant Called Lydia (Book 5)

A Friend Called Enoch (Book 6)

A Fisherman Called Simon (Book 7)

A Heroine Called Rahab (Book 8)

A Witness Called Mary (Book 9)

A Cupbearer Called Nehemiah (Book 10) - Coming Soon

To order your copy:

On your Kindle, click on the title in the list above,

Or go to: kenwinter.org/audiobooks

Or scan this QR code using your camera on your smartphone.

YOU WILL WANT TO READ ALL OF THE BOOKS IN "THE CALLED" SERIES

Stories of these ordinary men and women called by God to be used in extraordinary ways.

AVAILABLE IN PAPERBACK, LARGE PRINT, AND FOR KINDLE ON AMAZON.

Scan this QR code using your camera on your smartphone to see the entire series.

∾

THROUGH THE EYES

... the complete SERIES

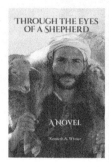  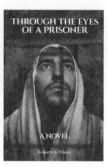

Experience the truths of Scripture as these stories unfold through the lives and eyes of a shepherd, a spy and a prisoner. Rooted in biblical truth, these fictional novels will enable you to draw beside the storytellers as they worship the Baby in the manger, the Son who took up the cross, the Savior who conquered the grave, the Deliverer who parted the sea and the Eternal God who has always had a mission.

Through the Eyes of a Shepherd (Book 1)

Through the Eyes of a Spy (Book 2)

Through the Eyes of a Prisoner (Book 3)

AVAILABLE IN PAPERBACK, LARGE PRINT, AND FOR KINDLE ON AMAZON.

Scan this QR code using your camera on your smartphone to see the entire series on Amazon:

THE EYEWITNESSES

… the complete collection

The first four books in these collections of short stories chronicle the first person eyewitness accounts of eighty-five men, women and children and their unique relationships with Jesus.

Little Did We Know – the advent of Jesus (Book 1)

Not Too Little To Know – the advent – ages 8 thru adult (Book 2)

The One Who Stood Before Us – the ministry and passion of Jesus (Book 3)

The Little Ones Who Came – the ministry and passion – ages 8 thru adult (Book 4)

The Patriarchs — eyewitnesses from the beginning — Adam through Moses tell their stories (Book 5) — releasing in 2024

AVAILABLE IN PAPERBACK, LARGE PRINT, AND FOR KINDLE ON AMAZON.

Scan this QR code using your camera on your smartphone to see the entire collection on Amazon:

LESSONS LEARNED IN THE WILDERNESS

the complete series

A non-fiction series of devotional studies

There are lessons that can only be learned in the wilderness experiences of our lives. As we see throughout the Bible, God is right there leading us each and every step of the way, if we will follow Him. Wherever we are, whatever we are experiencing, He will use it to enable us to experience His Person, witness His power and join Him in His mission.

The Journey Begins (Exodus) – Book 1

The Wandering Years (Numbers and Deuteronomy) – Book 2

Possessing The Promise (Joshua and Judges) – Book 3

Walking With The Master (The Gospels leading up to Palm Sunday) – Book 4

Taking Up The Cross (The Gospels – the passion through ascension) – Book 5

Until He Returns (The Book of Acts) – Book 6

The complete series is also available in two e-book boxsets or two single soft-cover print volumes.

Available in paperback and for Kindle on Amazon.

Scan this QR code using your camera on your smartphone to see the entire series on Amazon:

———————

For more information, go to:

wildernesslessons.com or kenwinter.org

ALSO AVAILABLE IN AUDIO

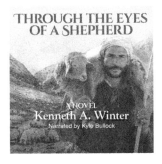

For more information on how you can order your audiobook, go to <u>kenwinter.org/</u> <u>audiobooks</u>

SCRIPTURE BIBLIOGRAPHY

～

The basis for the story line of this book is taken from the Books of Nehemiah, Ezra and Esther in the Holy Bible. Certain fictional events or depictions of those events have been added.

Some of the dialogue in this story are direct quotations from Scripture. Here are the specific references for those quotations:

Chapter 2

[1] Jeremiah 29:11

[2] Isaiah 44:23-26

Chapter 3

[1] Ezra 6:3, 8

[2] Esther 1:16-17, 19

[3] Esther 2:2, 4

Chapter 4

[1] Esther 4:14

Chapter 5

[1] Esther 4:11

[2] Esther 4:13-14

[3] Esther 4:16

Chapter 6

[1] Esther 5:3

[2] Esther 5:4

[3] Esther 5:5 – 8:17

Chapter 8

[1] Ezra 4:11-16

[2] Ezra 4:17-22

Chapter 10

[1] Nehemiah 1:5-11

[2] Nehemiah 2:2

[3] Nehemiah 2:3

Chapter 11

[1] Nehemiah 2:4

[2] Nehemiah 2:4

[3] Nehemiah 2:6

(4) Nehemiah 2:7

(5) Nehemiah 2:8

Chapter 12

(1) Nehemiah 2:17

(2) Nehemiah 2:18

(3) Nehemiah 2:19

(4) Nehemiah 2:20 (paraphrase)

(5) A record of all the assignments is included in Nehemiah 3:1-32

(6) Nehemiah 4:2

(7) Nehemiah 4:3

(8) Nehemiah 4:4-5

Chapter 13

(1) Nehemiah 4:10 (CEV)

(2) Nehemiah 4:14

(3) Nehemiah 4:20

(4) Nehemiah 5:2-4

(5) Nehemiah 5:5

(6) Nehemiah 5:8

(7) Nehemiah 5:10-11

(8) Nehemiah 5:12

(9) Nehemiah 5:13

Chapter 14

(1) Nehemiah 6:3

(2) Nehemiah 6:6-7

(3) Nehemiah 6:8

(4) Nehemiah 6:10

(5) Nehemiah 6:11

(6) Nehemiah 7:3 (paraphrase)

Chapter 15

(1) Nehemiah 8:6

(2) Nehemiah 8:9

(3) Nehemiah 8:10

(4) Nehemiah 8:15

(5) Nehemiah 9:5

(6) Nehemiah 9:27-28

(7) Nehemiah 9:31

(8) Nehemiah 9:36-37

(9) Nehemiah 9:38

Chapter 18

(1) Proverbs 24:21-22 (ESV)

Chapter 21

(1) Nehemiah 13:11

(2) Nehemiah 13:17-18

(3) Nehemiah 13:21

(4) 1 Kings 11:2 (NIV)

(5) Nehemiah 13:26-27

(6) Ezra 9:6-9 (paraphrase)

∽

LISTING OF CHARACTERS
(ALPHABETICAL ORDER)

~

Many of the characters in this book are real people pulled directly from the pages of Scripture. I have not changed any details about a number of those individuals except the addition of their interactions with the fictional characters. They are noted below as "UN" (unchanged).

In other instances, fictional details have been added to real people to provide backgrounds about their lives where Scripture is silent. The intent is that you understand these were real people, whose lives were full of all of the many details that fill our own lives. They are noted as "FB" (fictional background).

In some instances, we are never told the names of certain individuals in the Bible. In those instances, where i have given them a name as well as a fictional background, they are noted as "FN" (fictional name).

Lastly, a number of the characters are purely fictional, added to convey the fictional elements of these stories. They are noted as "FC" (fictional character).

~

Aaron – first high priest of Israel, older brother of Moses (UN)

Abihail – son of Shimei, father of Hadassah (Esther) (FB)

Abraham – patriarch of the Israelites (UN)

Agag – king of the Amalekites (UN)

Ahasuerus – *see Xerxes*

Artabanus – commander of King Xerxes's bodyguard (UN)

Artaxerxes – son of Xerxes, father of Darius II, fifth king of Persia 464-424 B.C. (FB)

Asaph – keeper of the Persian king's forest (UN)

Babak – governor of Memphis (FC)

Benjamin – son of Jacob (UN)

Bishlam – adversary of the rebuilding of Jerusalem (UN)

Cambyses II – son of Cyrus the Great, second king of Persia 530-522 B.C. (UN)

Cyrus the Great – first king of Persia 560-530 B.C. (UN)

Darius – third king of Persia 521-486 B.C. (UN)

Darius II – son of Artaxerxes, eighth king of Persia 423-404 B.C. (UN)

David – son of Jesse, second king of Israel (UN)

Eliashib – high priest, descendant of Aaron (FB)

Esther – *see Hadassah*

Ezer – father of Hacaliah, grandfather of Nehemiah, friend of Mordecai (FB)

Ezra – the scribe sent to restore the temple in Jerusalem (FB)

Geshem – chief of the Arab tribe who opposed Nehemiah (FB)

Hacaliah – son of Ezer, father of Nehemiah, Hanani, and three other sons (FB)

Hadassah/ Esther – daughter of Abihail, wife of Xerxes (FB)

Hadiya – wife of Hacaliah, mother of Hanani, Nehemiah, and other sons (FB)

Hallohesh – father of Shallum (UN)

Haman – Agagite prime minister of Persia under Xerxes (UN)

Hanan – son of Zaccur, governor of Jerusalem (FB)

Hanani – oldest son of Hacaliah, brother of Nehemiah (FB)

Hananiah – perfume maker, worked on Jerusalem wall (UN)

Hanun – city leader of Zanoah, worked on Jerusalem wall (UN)

Harhaiah – father of Uzziel, the goldsmith (UN)

Hegai – eunuch in charge of royal harem (FB)

Inaros – Egyptian who led revolt against Persia (UN)

Isaac – son of Abraham, patriarch of the Israelites (UN)

Isaiah – prophet of God (UN)

Izak – replaced Nehemiah as cupbearer to the king (FC)

Jacob – son of Isaac, patriarch of the Israelites (UN)

Jair – son of Shimei, father of Mordecai (FB)

Jehohanan – son of Tobiah (UN)

Jeremiah – prophet of God (UN)

Joiada – son of Eliashib (UN)

Joshua – son of Nun, chosen by God to lead His people into the Promised Land (UN)

Judah – son of Jacob (UN)

Kish – father of Shimei (FB)

Malachi – prophet of God, member of the Great Synagogue (FB)

Malkijah – goldsmith, worked on Jerusalem wall (UN)

Manasseh – husband of Nikaso, priest of Samaritan temple (FN)

Meshullam – worked on the Jerusalem wall (UN)

Mithredath – adversary of rebuilding Jerusalem (UN)

Mordecai – son of Jair, prime minister of Persia under Xerxes and Artaxerxes (FB)

Moses – chosen by God to lead His people out of Egypt (UN)

Nebuchadnezzar II (the Great) – son of Nabopolassar, king of Babylon, 605-562 B.C. (UN)

Nehemiah – cupbearer to the king, sent to rebuild the walls and restore Jerusalem FB)

Nikaso – daughter of Sanballat, wife of Manasseh (FN)

Nun – father of Joshua (UN)

Pedaiah – Levite given responsibility over temple storerooms (UN)

Rehum – chancellor of a western province (UN)

Sanballat – Horonite governor of Samaria (FB)

Shallum – son of Hallohesh, worked on the wall (UN)

Shapur – prime minister of Persia under Artaxerxes (FC)

Shecaniah – priest who accompanied Zerubbabel (UN)

Shelemiah – high priest, descendant of Aaron (UN)

Shemaiah – prophet who attempts to deceive Nehemiah (UN)

Shimei – son of Kish, father of Abihail and Jair (FB)

Shimshai – scribe of Rehum (UN)

Solomon – son of David, third king of Israel (UN)

Tabeel – adversary of the work to rebuild Jerusalem (UN)

Tobiah – Ammonite who opposed Nehemiah (FB)

Unnamed daughter of Meshullam – wife of Jehohanan (UN)

Unnamed governor of Cunaxa – governor of a western province (UN)

Unnamed great grandparents of Nehemiah – parents of Ezer (FC)

Unnamed officers who accompanied Nehemiah – officers sent by Artaxerxes (UN)

Unnamed three sons of Hacaliah – brothers of Nehemiah (FC)

Unnamed wife of Abihail – mother of Hadassah (FB)

Uzziel – son of Harhaiah, goldsmith, worked on Jerusalem wall (UN)

Vashti – queen to King Xerxes, mother of Artaxerxes, banished from the palace (FB)

Xerxes/ Ahasuerus – fourth king of Persia 485-465 B.C. (FB)

Zaccur – father of Hanan (UN)

Zadok – scribe given responsibility over temple storerooms (UN)

Zerubbabel – the governor sent to restore Jerusalem, grandson of King Jeconiah (FB)

∾

ACKNOWLEDGMENTS

I do not cease to give thanks for you ....
Ephesians 1:16 (ESV)

… my partner and best friend, LaVonne,
for choosing to trust God as we walk together with Him in this faith
adventure;

… my family,
for your continuing love, support and encouragement;

… Sheryl,
for your partnership in the work;

… Scott,
for using the gifts God has given you;

… a precious group of advance readers,
who encourage and challenge me in the journey;

… and most importantly,
the One who goes before me in all things
– my Lord and Savior Jesus Christ!

∼

A WORD OF EXPLANATION FOR THOSE OF YOU WHO ARE NEW TO MY WRITING

You will notice that whenever i use the pronoun "I" referring to myself, i have chosen to use a lowercase "i." This only applies to me personally (in the Preface). i do not impose my personal conviction on any of the characters in this book. It is not a typographical error. i know this is contrary to proper English grammar and accepted editorial style guides. But years ago, the Lord convicted me – personally – that in all things i must decrease and He must increase. And as a way of continuing personal reminder, from that day forward, i have chosen to use a lowercase "i" whenever referring to myself.

Because of the same conviction, i use a capital letter for any pronoun referring to God. The style guide for most translations of Scripture do not share that conviction. However, you will see that i have intentionally made that slight revision and capitalized any pronoun referring to God in any quotations of Scripture. Please accept my apology for any style guide violations , but i must honor this conviction.

Lastly, regarding this matter – this is a <u>personal</u> conviction – and i share it only so you will understand why i have chosen to deviate from normal editorial practice. i am in no way suggesting or endeavoring to have anyone else subscribe to my conviction. Thank you for your understanding.

ABOUT THE AUTHOR

 Ken Winter is a follower of Jesus, an extremely blessed husband, and a proud father and grandfather – all by the grace of God. His journey with Jesus has led him to serve on the pastoral staffs of two local churches – one in West Palm Beach, Florida and the other in Richmond, Virginia – and as the vice president of mobilization of the IMB, an international missions organization.

Today, Ken continues in that journey as a full-time author, teacher and speaker. You can read his weekly blog posts at kenwinter.blog and listen to his weekly podcast at kenwinter.org/podcast.

And we proclaim Him, admonishing every man and teaching every man with all wisdom, that we may present every man complete in Christ. And for this purpose also I labor, striving according to His power, which mightily works within me.
(Colossians 1:28-29 NASB)

PLEASE JOIN MY READERS' GROUP

Please join my Readers' Group in order to receive updates and information about future releases, etc.

Also, i will send you a free copy of *The Journey Begins* e-book — the first book in the *Lessons Learned In The Wilderness* series. It is yours to keep or share with a friend or family member that you think might benefit from it.

It's completely free to sign up. i value your privacy and will not spam you. Also, you can unsubscribe at any time.

Go to kenwinter.org to subscribe.

Or scan this QR code using your camera on your smartphone:

~